Books by Rex Warner

THE YOUNG CAESAR

IMPERIAL CAESAR

PERICLES THE ATHENIAN

PERICLES
THE
ATHENIAN

PERICLES
THE
ATHENIAN

□□□□□□□□□□□□□□□□□□□□□□□□□□□□□□□□□□□

by Rex Warner

An Atlantic Monthly Press Book

LITTLE, BROWN AND COMPANY • BOSTON • TORONTO

LIBRARY OF CONGRESS CATALOG CARD NO. 63–8311

FIRST EDITION

ATLANTIC–LITTLE, BROWN BOOKS
ARE PUBLISHED BY
LITTLE, BROWN AND COMPANY
IN ASSOCIATION WITH
THE ATLANTIC MONTHLY PRESS

Published simultaneously in Canada
by Little, Brown & Company (Canada) Limited

PRINTED IN THE UNITED STATES OF AMERICA

What I would prefer is that you should fix your eyes every day on the greatness of Athens as she really is, and should fall in love with her.

PERICLES

Contents

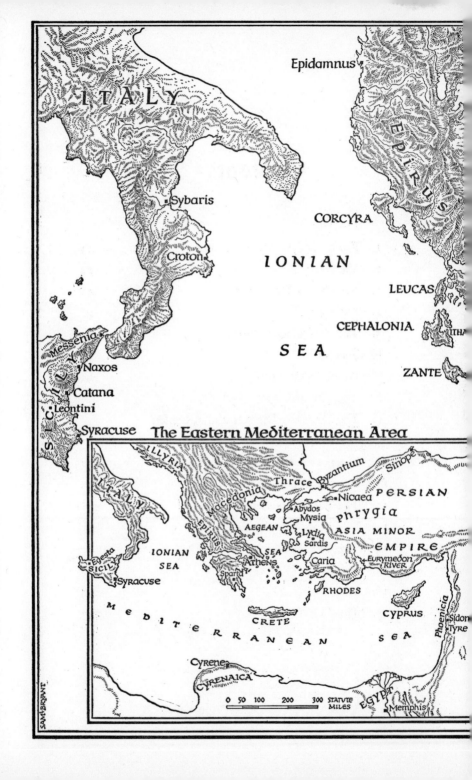

The Eastern Mediterranean Area

The Aegean World

STATUTE MILES
50   25   0   50   100

50   0   50   100
KILOMETERS

PERICLES
THE
ATHENIAN

Prologue

Anaxagoras of Clazomenai, the philosopher, writes to some members of the Town Council of Lampsacus.

YOU DO me great honor, my friends, in asking me to write down, for the instruction of future ages, some account of the thoughts and actions of Pericles the Athenian, the news of whose death we have just heard. And I have at least two reasons for being delighted to do as you ask. In the first place, Pericles was my pupil and my friend; he saved my life. Had it not been for him I should never have reached this agreeable city of Lampsacus. It is therefore fitting that I should wish to commemorate and, so far as I can, make immortal a man to whom I owe so much, and for whom I feel such regard. But I have other motives, not at all of a personal nature, which impel me to write of this great man. For it is my belief that, of all the Greeks of our time, he will be found to have been the most daring, the most resolute and the most intelligent. Thus, apart altogether from the charm of his nature and the brilliance of his achievements, he is a character of philosophical importance.

The claims I am making for him are, I admit, great. Obviously, it may be said, Pericles was inferior to Themistocles or to Kimon as a general, to Aeschylus or to Sophocles as a poet, to me or to Parmenides as a philosopher.

What then? Facts such as these do not prevent him from being superior to us all. As I have been careful to point out in my philosophical work, there are elements of everything in everything, though one characteristic, if sufficiently emphasized, will determine the appearance of the whole. Thus one may be known and seen in the light of some particular skill or particular enthusiasm, if that skill or enthusiasm is great or brilliant enough. In man, however, all skills, beauties, aspirations and endeavors are in a very special way (which I have explained elsewhere) subject to intelligence. It is intelligence which causes motion and directs the whole. And this it is which in Pericles I most notice and most admire — a general force of intelligence pervading his nature, powerful in so many directions at once, pure, unmixed with the sordid, extending beyond the moment, irresistible.

All this may be admitted. All this is, indeed, obvious to those who, like myself, have seen the intelligence of the man in action, who have watched him in the Assembly of the Athenians, justifying to these hotheaded, volatile, yet keen-minded and resolute men some unpopular policy or guiding them, as though they were sleepwalkers, in some direction which they had never imagined. If one can control Athenians, one can control anything; and here even Pericles sometimes had his setbacks. Yet on the whole his dominance was complete; and on the whole (though of course there were occasions when he appealed to the people's greed or ambition) this dominance was exercised by reason — clear, vehement and sincere. He shaped the mass — separating, combining, putting in order — like that intelligence which, in my philosophy, is the cause of the appearance of everything and of all worlds.

This in itself may seem to be enough to justify one in describing Pericles as "great." Yet there are still questions which may be and no doubt will be asked: Was this intelligence used wisely, and in the best and truest interests of his country and of himself? Will his work prove to be lasting or ephemeral? Was the empire that he created really as splendid as he imagined, or was it, as the Spartans and their allies say, a tyranny?

Athens is now at war, and there is no doubt that Pericles himself led his country into this war, the issue of which remains uncertain. It is possible that in the course of this war Athens will be destroyed. It is also possible that the whole of Greece will be so weakened by this struggle that she will be left an easy prey to Persia or to some other barbarian power as yet unknown. In the boyhood of Pericles, it may be said, Greece was united and glorious; at the time of his death Greece has split into two furiously hostile camps. For this state of affairs he is certainly, in a large measure, responsible. May we not say, therefore, that his admittedly great intelligence was misapplied, that his organization was in the direction of chaos?

A difficult question, my friends, but not, I think, insolvable. Let us remember that what appears is not the truth of the matter. What appears is, as I have written elsewhere, a mere vision of the unseen. At first impression, our ordinary, unaided senses are too weak to enable us to judge the truth. But this does not mean that truth is inaccessible to us. Reflection and experiment can detect error and discover order. I well remember how, when I was quite a young man and Pericles only a boy, I demonstrated to him, by the simple experiment of inflating wineskins with bellows, that air is corporeal. Yet we are accustomed to think of it as mere emptiness. Pericles, with his usual quickness of mind, immediately grasped the general principles involved. I do not mean simply that he recognized the obvious fact that appearances are deceptive. No, his mind ranged further than that. "If," he asked me, "there is no empty space in the universe, how can one thing be separated from another thing? How can one thing come into existence and another cease to be? How can there be any motion?" I believe that at that time he had had no instruction in philosophy, yet in a flash he saw the essentials of the problem with which Parmenides, Empedocles and I have been chiefly occupied.

I used to think that I had solved this problem. Now I am not so sure. Yet I remain perfectly convinced of the validity of my method, the scientific method which was discovered, for the first time in human history, in my native country of Ionia. All things are subject to the same laws, though these laws will operate in diverse ways. All perception, for instance, is produced by opposites and all sensation must imply pain. Yet perception, at its best, is clear and distinct; and sensation is often pleasurable. We live in a world of contradictions, and these contradictions are as evident in human affairs as they are in the movements or constitutions of the heavenly bodies. But we Greek philosophers have made the assumption (perhaps the most daring assumption ever made) that all these contradictions are subject to general law and will be found to be in the end capable of explanation.

Now, with regard to history and social organization, our knowledge, our speculation and our practice are less advanced and much less precise than in the cases of, say, mathematics or physics. Moreover, there is an important difference between the former and the latter subjects. The life of man must be not only studied, but lived. And to be lived adequately, it must be consciously shaped towards certain ends. Not all ends are possible. Man, for example, cannot live the life of a reptile or a bird. He is subject, too, to various pressures of external nature. He must find food to keep himself alive. He must fortify himself against his enemies. These and other essentials for survival have often been regarded as of such importance that the whole of human endeavor has been devoted to securing them. Many men, in all states, think of nothing, from the cradle to the grave, except how to acquire the money which will ensure them food, shelter, and safety. Great powers, such as Sparta, have been organized entirely on the basis of military domination over neighbors who, unless terrified, would revolt. Nor can one say that these limited ways of life are without virtue. The Spartan is certainly brave; the hard-working businessman contributes grain, oil and other necessities to his countrymen. But the businessman, occupied entirely with his own affairs, is seldom a good judge of music, literature or philosophy; and the Spartan, as I have often observed, loses all his virtue as soon as he is removed from the familiar environment of his armed camp. These limited, restricted lives, lived without reference to the more numerous and engaging aspects of human nature, have never appealed greatly to any of us Ionians. But it must be owned that often, when confronted with what has seemed to us a solid stupidity, we, with our greater daring, initiative, variety and intelligence, have somehow, because of a central weakness, collapsed.

Pericles, as he was the greatest Athenian, was also the greatest Ionian. He was never, as Kimon was, deluded into the sentimental belief that brute force and discipline are in themselves superior to intelligence and versatility. Hence his lifelong opposition to Sparta. Yet he would never belittle the qualities that are known, rather incorrectly, as specifically Dorian. His aim was rather to incorporate these qualities (and to intensify them) in a character which would be, for this time and for all times, specifically Athenian. In the Athens which he loved, the soldier would be as brave on the field of battle as any Spartan; but his courage would spring from reflection, knowledge of what was at stake, a natural and self-imposed discipline rather than from the doggedness that comes from years of arduous training or the emulation that is a form of self-regard. Pericles did not hold the view that one virtue is incompatible with another. His ideal Athenian would possess all the virtues and he would carry them with a peculiar grace and a peculiar versatility. The Athenian was to be like a god — only a god with a city and with work to do.

Athens, of course, was not the creation of Pericles. The qualities which Pericles admired and sought to intensify were in existence before his birth and had triumphantly revealed themselves in action during his boyhood. For the disciplined enterprise of Athens had more to do with the defeat of the Persians than had the selfish and unenterprising courage of Sparta. What Pericles did was deliberately to accelerate a process that had already begun. The greatness of his intelligence is shown in the facts that he was, more than all others, conscious of this process and that, in advancing it, he chose (within the limits which must bound any human action) precisely the best and most appropriate means. It is scarcely too much to say that he was in Athens producing something which almost amounted to a new race of men. How successful he was, it will be for posterity to judge. For myself, if I might hazard a guess, I should say that future ages will wonder at Athens as we wonder at her now; and whatever the result of the present war, I should maintain this view. And if I am asked, "Did Pericles disrupt Greece?" I shall answer, "No. Greece was already disrupted. The mind of man has always been disrupted. What Pericles did was to make a choice; and in doing so, he acted like a creator."

These assertions of mine, my friends, may possibly surprise you, as they seem to lack evidence for their support. I shall attempt in what I write to provide the evidence in the way that seems to me most honest and most satisfactory. I shall relate the facts, so far as they are known to me, and I shall not attempt to conceal anything which may conflict with an easy or personal or short-cutting explanation. Things are not cut off short with a hatchet; and those of you who have any experience of my philosophy will know that in any assessment of any event or situation I expect contradiction. But I search for and I adore truth.

And now in approaching my subject I ask myself how best may the truth be discovered and imparted. Obviously I must narrate all those significant events in the life of Pericles which are known to me either from personal experience or from the trustworthy accounts of others. But I must also, I think, do rather more than this. None of us is wholly free from prejudice and partiality; and I, in this case, should at least indicate the angle from which my observations are being made. More important still, I must not treat Pericles as an isolated object in space. He is as connected with the past as he is with the future. I must at least make some reference to the old history out of which he created the new.

Now my viewpoint is that of an Ionian who has spent most of his life in Athens. And it so happens that I played a small part in some of those great events which were the background to the boyhood of Pericles. I accompanied the Persian expedition to Greece and was an eyewitness of some of the actions of the war. If, therefore, I begin my account of Pericles in what may be described as an autobiographical manner, you will not, I hope, my friends, consider that I am doing this from vanity. I am merely adopting what seems to me to be the most scientific method for my purpose, which is an investigation, not of myself, but of Pericles. As I approach the period when Pericles began to enter upon political life, I shall try to write in such a way that you will scarcely know that I exist.

1

□□□□□

From Clazomenai to Salamis

THEY SAY, "Each man his city," but I have had three
cities and for all of them I feel loyalty and affection.
Now I am privileged in enjoying the citizenship here at
Lampsacus and here I hope that I shall spend my declining
years. At Athens, of course, I never was a full citizen. This
was a right most jealously guarded by the Athenians and
not least by Pericles himself. Yet still I felt that Athens was
my city, the city of all Ionians, the city of all Hellenes.
And this is what Pericles wished us to feel.

But I was born at Clazomenai, on the Greek coast of
Asia, in sight of the sea, the long headlands, the immensely
varying sky. Clazomenai, as you know, is one of the twelve
Ionian cities, and my father, a man of some wealth, often
undertook official duties at our temple, the Panionion, to
the south of us, opposite Samos. He played his part too in
the great Ionian revolt against Persia which took place soon
after my birth. Naturally I remember nothing of this revolt, but in my childhood nurses, relatives and friends
would constantly be telling me stories of it — of how the
Ionian army had made a daring march inland and had

burned the Persian capital of Sardis and of how the news of this brilliant success had roused up the Greek cities from the far south of Asia Minor as far as the Dardanelles to fight for their liberty and for the great days before the coming of the Persians. Even before the attack on Sardis — indeed, at the very beginning of the revolt — Athens, though engaged at the time in war with the neighboring island of Aegina, had boldly sent to us, her kinsmen, a large proportion of her fleet and a considerable force of infantry. Sparta had done nothing to help us. I heard many stories of the heroism displayed by the Ionians in the four or five years of active resistance which ended in the great naval battle off Miletus, where our fleet of triremes numbered no less than three hundred and fifty — the largest Greek fleet that had ever put to sea. In the stories which I heard I was encouraged to admire the performances of my people, and indeed, as boys will, I did admire anything worthy which had any connection with myself. But on closer reflection I found little to admire except individual actions. I could discover no guiding intelligence in the affair. It struck me as remarkable that the Athenians, after having helped us in the opening and most dangerous stages of the revolt, subsequently withdrew their support, and it occurred to me that they might have correctly estimated the situation — a situation in which many states were more interested in securing advantages over their neighbors than in defeating the enemy. There was no unity of command and, after the beginning, little initiative was shown. On the other hand, the Persian armies on land operated, evidently, with great intelligence, and in the naval battle at Lade it was the Persians, not the Greeks, who attacked. Indeed, most of the great Greek fleet dispersed even before battle was joined. This was not because we lacked courage, but because we were not infused with that guiding intelligence which promotes resolution and achieves results. How different it was in that sea battle, fought near the same place some fifteen years later, when Pericles's father Xanthippus, leading an Athenian fleet, recovered our liberty at Mycale!

For failing to show a sufficiently patriotic enthusiasm for the Ionian revolt, I was later accused before the Athenian courts of being pro-Persian, though of course the really serious charge against me was that of impiety. Needless to say, both charges were false. I sympathized with those of my fellow countrymen who had died bravely, though on investigation, it seemed to me certain that they had died aimlessly or, at any rate, with an aim not sufficiently defined. It was indeed a tragedy, but a tragedy that was not entirely worthy. I was much moved when I heard of what had happened in Athens at a dramatic festival just after the collapse of the revolt and the capture of Miletus. The playwright Phrynichus had put on a play describing these final events and the whole audience had been moved to tears. They had then fined Phrynichus a large sum of money and had passed a decree forbidding any future performance of his play.

I myself was lucky to have been so young at this time, as in the cities recaptured by the Persians many of the boys not greatly older than myself were castrated and sent back to serve as eunuchs at the king's court or in the palaces of Persian noblemen. Many of the girls also were sent away, but their fate may at least be described as being in accordance with nature.

At Clazomenai, however, which was one of the first of the cities to be reoccupied by the Persians, the reprisals were not heavy and did not last long. I myself can remember no inconvenience of any kind. In general, I believe that the Persian policy towards the Greek cities was wise and tolerant. In most of these cities democratic governments

were established with the aid of Persian influence; the
taxes were not excessive; and many Greeks found positions
of trust and honor at the Persian court. Indeed King Da-
rius, who was by all accounts not only an admirable administrator but a good and honorable man, welcomed and
protected Greeks from the mainland as well as from the
Ionian cities. He had with him, of course, from Athens
the sons of Pisistratus, the great dictator, and from Sparta
the exiled King Demaratus, an extremely intelligent man
for a Spartan, and the only Spartan king who had ever
won the chariot race at Olympia. And there were others too
who, without being exiled, still chose to serve the Great
King. It is not surprising, then, that to most of us during
my childhood and early youth, it seemed natural and inevitable that the vast and, on the whole, beneficent power
of Persia should overwhelm the world. We were wrong, but
there was at that time little evidence to prove us wrong.

Yet now, when I look back, I can see that even this
scanty evidence should have been sufficient. The kings of
Persia have often had brave soldiers and good generals;
they have often themselves been wise, farsighted and ambitious. Yet all the intelligence (that guiding principle of
creation) has come, as it were, from the top. It has not
been interfused with the mass. The Persians obey laws;
they do not make them. Politically they lack integration,
even of a low order, as Pericles would say. For Pericles was
perfectly well aware of the integration of courage and intelligence that was to be found in Sparta. Yet his own ideas
of integration (a notion towards which I think, in our
early philosophizing, I may have tended to guide him)
were of a different order altogether. However, the fact that
should have been evident in theory even before it was
proved in practice is that mere numbers are not in themselves irresistible. This is obvious, but we tend through

habit often to neglect the obvious. We had seen the Persians so constantly and widely victorious that we could conceive no end to the process.

By the time that I was eight years old the Great King's son-in-law Mardonius had advanced as far as Macedonia. Next year a seaborne expedition set out from Samos towards Athens and Euboea. There were many Ionians serving aboard the ships and I can still remember hearing firsthand accounts of how the enormous Persian force had been utterly routed by the Athenians at Marathon. It was a portent, but scarcely anyone recognized it as such. We too, we reflected, had once won a victory over the Persians, but we had suffered for it later. Moreover, looking at Athens from a distance and observing her inaccurately, we seemed to detect in her the same symptoms of internal confusion which had helped to weaken us. The victor of Marathon, Miltiades, the father of Kimon, was prosecuted and fined, and died in disgrace within a year of the battle. Among his prosecutors was Xanthippus, the father of Pericles. And in subsequent years other important Athenians, including Xanthippus himself, were driven into honorable exile by that peculiar Athenian device of ostracism, by which if sufficient votes are cast against any individual, that individual is forced to leave the country for ten years. These ostracisms are not so stupid as they sound. Usually it is a question of choosing between two able statesmen with divergent policies, and the Athenians believe that if one policy rather than another is preferred, it will be best carried out when its most notorious opponent is unable to interfere. And in these years the policy of the Athenian democracy was consistent, though we in Ionia were not aware of it.

Later on I was able to talk to many of those who had fought at Marathon, including the poet Aeschylus, whose brother died most gallantly in the battle. I found that these men were, on the whole, less interested in the great names and the great clans than I had expected. Their views differed widely (an Athenian is always versatile) and yet on certain subjects there was unanimity and the resolution that is born of it. They believed in this new democracy of theirs, and they believed in Athenian virtue or excellence. All they differed upon was the means by which it might be displayed. Of course there were also, as there have always been at Athens, keen personal rivalries. In these years the number of ostracisms alone will indicate the bitterness of these rivalries. Fortunately, however, both for Athens and for Greece, the statesman who showed the greatest power of survival was the most far-sighted and the most consistent of them all. This was Themistocles, a new man, unconnected with any of the noble families, yet in his policies and his intelligence the precursor of Pericles himself. It was Themistocles who first saw that the future of Athens was upon the sea. He created Athenian naval power, and in doing so he widened the basis of Athenian democracy; for in a naval power the sailor, who need possess nothing, is at least as important as the man rich enough to afford the equipment of a cavalryman or a hoplite. Pericles, with greater enlightenment and greater social prestige, was to follow in the path of Themistocles and was to preserve for far longer a position of ascendancy, but no one, not even Pericles himself, showed greater practical intelligence than did Themistocles in these years of the Persian peril.

To us in Clazomenai, however, even the name of Themistocles was, in the nine years after Marathon, virtually unknown. Athens we knew and respected as the motherland of Ionians. We admired her for her resistance at Marathon, but we scarcely envied her her probable fate. When I myself imagined the possibilities of settling in any other city I would think always of the Greek cities in the west, in Sicily or Italy, where it seemed that philosophy, born in Ionia, was now taking on a new life. For even in my boyhood I was, in my way, a philosopher, and long before my boyhood was over I paid reverence in my own mind not to the great dynasts but to the philosophers of my country. Polycrates of Samos had ruled the sea, and even in my childhood the splendor of his court had become a legend. But Thales of Miletus had ventured to ask, for the first time in history, a scientific question. Others, even under the Persian conquest, had continued his work at Miletus. I myself had listened to those who had been taught by Anaximenes. I had been delighted by the daring common sense of Xenophanes, a native of nearby Colophon, who in a few short sentences made clear to me how absurd and unworthy are man's views of the gods. For why should a god be in human form, and why should he speak Greek? One must note, however, that Xenophanes fails to give any account of motion. I had also discussed Pythagoras with my friends and had found him unsatisfactory. Some thirty years before my birth he had left Samos and settled in southern Italy. There even today his followers have not only an intellectual, but a political influence. Their influence proceeds, I think, from the fact that they form a kind of secret brotherhood rather than from any political or scientific merits of their own. They combine admirable mathematical skill with a kind of superstition. Their discoveries in geometry are remarkable, but for some reason best known to themselves, they refuse to eat beans and would almost rather die than touch a white cock. Our great Ionian philosopher Heracleitus of Ephesus was right when he wrote: "The learning of many things does not teach understanding. Otherwise it would have taught Pythagoras and Xenophanes."

Heracleitus was the last of the Ionian philosophers with whose work I became acquainted in my boyhood and early youth. I still find him strangely impressive, though as I grow wiser I have less and less of an idea of what he means. He, as much as any of the others, excited me to the pursuit of wisdom. How often, lying in the sun or shade along the reedy banks of streams that go down to Clazomenai and the open sea and sky, have I repeated to myself over and over again, "Wisdom is one thing. It is to know the thought by which all things are steered through all things." And I became somewhat indifferent to my father's plans for me. I had no wish to be excessively burdened by public duties and by the management of an estate. I watched the stars, animals and birds, the sky and the sea. In the end, I was determined, I would give up my estate and devote my life to science, possibly in some Ionian city, possibly in one of the Greek cities of Italy or Sicily. But first I wished to travel and to see something of the world. It was for this reason that, at the age of eighteen, I took part in Xerxes's expedition against Greece.

And here, since I have been accused of being pro-Persian, a few words of explanation are necessary. Now, when all the islands and the Greek coast of Asia have been liberated (or, at least, are subject to Athens rather than to a foreign power), it may seem strange or even wicked to imagine a situation in which Greeks in the service of Persia marched against their fellow Greeks. But to us at the time it did not seem strange. We Ionians who, whether voluntarily or by compulsion, found ourselves in the Great King's forces did not expect, in fact, any fighting at all. According to the reports which reached us, all Greece,

except Athens and Sparta, had already sent tokens of submission — earth and water — to Persia; and these reports
were not greatly exaggerated. It was expected that the expedition of Xerxes would be rather a triumphal procession
than a military campaign. Nor were we conscious of any
real opposition to our fellow countrymen. There were
many Greeks with Xerxes ready to regain power in states
from which, for one reason or another, they had been
exiled. The whole operation (so it seemed to us) would
certainly end in an extension of the Great King's domin-
ions, but in practical terms of Greek politics only in the
substitution of one party for another.

We were, of course, wrong, and I myself am certainly
ashamed to think of how lacking I was in political and
indeed scientific perception. It is true that older and wiser
men than I were at least equally mistaken, but I have never
regarded the stupidity of others as any excuse for my own.
I should on this point prefer to excuse my insensitivity
rather on the grounds that I did not think at all than that I
thought like everyone else.

Indeed, when I rode out from Clazomenai to join the
king's army in Sardis I thought of little except the excitement of foreign travel. And in the king's army itself
there was enough to excite any inquiring intelligence.
This army included almost every race in the known world.
I was told that more than five hundred languages were in
use. And not only in language but in dress, equipment,
armor, pigmentation, custom and religion there was an
extraordinary variety. The Persian soldiers were, of course,
familiar to me, with their trousers and mail coats, which
looked like the scales of a fish; but I looked with amazement at contingents of other peoples of whom, up to then,
I had known nothing — the Assyrians with their bronze
helmets and wooden clubs studded with iron, the Indians

with their cotton dresses and cane bows, the Ethiopians, who carried shields made from the skins of cranes and who wore on their heads horses' scalps with the ears and manes dangling behind. Innumerable others too; but this is not the place to describe either the army or the march through Asia, over the Hellespont and into Greece. These events have already been well described by my young friend Herodotus, who was himself a baby at this time, and who has often in later years spent hours with me in Athens, questioning me on every detail of the expedition. With his great skill and considerable intelligence he has, I think, produced a literary masterpiece, though I doubt whether it deserved that enormous monetary prize which it was awarded, through the influence of Pericles, at Athens. The book is still in immense demand and people are prepared to pay exorbitant prices for it, whereas my own works on philosophy are available at Athens for the modest price of one drachma.

Personally I am delighted with young Herodotus's success and I am glad that I have, in a minor way, contributed to it. I wish, however, that in some ways he had adopted a more scientific attitude. I remember telling him, for instance, of the so-called skin of Marsyas, which is on show in the Phrygian city of Celaenai. Tourists are encouraged to admire this as the skin of the satyr, or silenus, Marsyas, who was flayed by Apollo after unsuccessfully competing with him in music. Now, as I told Herodotus, I have myself identified this skin as the skin of a rare species of Cappadocian mountain goat. Moreover, my studies in anatomy and reproduction have led me to believe that it is extremely unlikely that such creatures as satyrs have ever existed. But Herodotus, in his history, makes no mention of my identification of the skin. He prefers to subscribe to superstition by merely repeating the local story. However, in general, his work is greatly to be admired and his account of Xerxes's expedition is excellent. Certainly there is no need for me now to recall to you in detail those tremendous experiences which he has so well described. Few, however, who have not seen it can imagine that great bridge across the Hellespont, packed with all the nations of the east marching to the conquest of Europe. And as we went on through Thrace and into Thessaly, we were joined by more and more contingents of troops — Greeks, Macedonians, Thracians and strange tribes from the unknown interior. Physically speaking, it appeared that this force was wholly irresistible.

There were indeed three unexpected events. First the great storm in which four hundred ships of the king's navy were destroyed; then the heroic resistance of the Spartans and their allies at Thermopylae; and, no less important, the fact that the small Greek fleet, consisting mostly of Athenian vessels, was able to engage the king's fleet in the narrow waters between Euboea and the mainland and to hold its own. But these events were not decisive or even, it seemed, very important. The Spartan position was turned and the Persian fleet, even after the storm, was still more than three times as strong as any fleet that could be found to oppose it.

So the army moved south into Attica, encountering no resistance. Late in the summer we came to Athens and found it deserted except for a few old men and temple attendants who, in a mistaken faith in an oracle, had barricaded themselves on the Acropolis. Their defense was soon overwhelmed and those of them who did not commit suicide were massacred. Then the temples on the Acropolis were set on fire and Xerxes sent a messenger back to Susa to announce to Persia that his victory, at least so far as the Athenians were concerned, was complete.

It was at this time that I, with a few other Ionians who shared my views, deserted the king's army and, after having bribed the captain of one of the small craft attached to the king's fleet, sailed across to Salamis, where the Athenian fleet was based and where most of the Athenian non-combatants had taken refuge. Our action sprang, I think, rather from the natural adventurousness of youth than from any nobler motive. It is true that we had begun to feel somewhat ashamed at the prospect of having to fight our fellow countrymen. Here, perhaps, the propaganda of Themistocles had affected us. For, owing to his instructions, there had been engraved or painted on the rocks, both on the land and sea routes by which the Persians had advanced, appeals to the Greeks serving in the army or fleet not to incur the guilt of helping to destroy their own mother country. There were also assurances that final victory would go to the Greeks and that those who had collaborated with the Persians would be punished. Few, I think, believed these assurances. We did not know precisely what would happen, but certainly anticipated a Persian conquest of the mainland. As for ourselves, we hoped that if we survived we should have an opportunity of sailing westward, to Italy or Sicily, either to some Greek city already established or to some new settlement which would be founded by the Athenians to replace their own city now occupied and half destroyed by the Persians. It did not occur to me that I should spend the greater part of my adult life in a new Athens, far more glorious than the old, and established on the same spot.

So we reached Salamis and were welcomed both for ourselves (my father had certain relations of hospitality with some of the leading Athenian families) and for the information which we brought with regard to the Persian forces. Among those who questioned me was Xanthippus, the father of Pericles. He had been in exile, but had been recalled in the general amnesty of the year before. He behaved most generously to me, and it was through him that I made the acquaintance of Pericles himself, then a boy of about fourteen.

2

□□□□□

Victories

I CAN SEE HIM now as I saw him then — a boy of quite extraordinary beauty, of unusual intelligence and of the sweetest disposition. When I met him first (and we made friends at once) he was angry and embittered, but in his anger and his bitterness there was nothing uncouth, nothing coarse, nothing stupid. He was angry about his dog, and in his anger there were several points that I found remarkable. First, the anger had lasted for some weeks (an unusual thing in a boy of his age); and then his feeling, while intense, was, in a way, generalized. He bitterly disapproved of his father's behavior in this instance, but without any real personal animosity. His attitude was like that of a god who condemns and perhaps violently punishes the deed while looking calmly on the doer of it. Yet he was not aloof (as gods are said to be) and was far from being insensitive.

It appears that what had happened was this. When evacuating his family and household from his estate near Athens to Salamis, Xanthippus had given orders that no animals were to be taken aboard the first boat. Horses, hounds and other livestock were to be ferried over later, supposing transport to be available. It was a sensible enough order, considering the shortage of space, but one of the hounds, a particular favorite of Pericles's, refused to be left behind. This animal sprang into the water and began to swim after the ship, which, of course, rapidly went ahead. Soon nothing could be seen but a speck in the distance, which was the dog's head, and in the general hurry and confusion, no one would listen to Pericles's entreaties and demands that they should put about and rescue the creature. Unavailing attempts were made to reassure the boy by pointing out that the dog would soon get tired and swim back again. In fact the dog did nothing of the kind. By some sense, whether of sight or smell, he kept contact with the vessel for the whole distance, and when they had nearly finished unloading the cargo at Salamis, he was to be seen again still swimming toward the shore. Pericles, and Xanthippus too, ran down to the beach in delight to welcome the animal. But the dog was exhausted. He crawled up on to the sand, put back his ears, as though expecting to be stroked, collapsed and died. I was told that for a week after this Pericles would not speak to his elder brother Ariphron, who had taken the event lightly. He was furious too with his father, whom he regarded as responsible for the death, though in the end he became mollified when Xanthippus, who was genuinely sorry for the boy and at the same time proud of the distinction won by the dog, had a tomb built for the animal on the shores of Salamis. It is to be seen there to this day.

I mention this incident in order to illustrate an aspect of Pericles's character which is not generally known. People who saw him only in public are apt to think of him as austere or, as they used to say, "Olympian"; they do not recognize that tenderheartedness of his which was very evident in his private relationships and which extended, as we have seen, even to animals.

It was in the company of Pericles that from some high ground in Salamis I watched the great naval battle in the straits. The boy was eager to be in the fighting himself. So indeed was I; but the ships were already fully manned. I had no equipment, and so was given some small administrative post ashore. Xanthippus, of course, was in command of a trireme and Pericles's elder brother was with him.

The battle has been well described by both Herodotus and Aeschylus, but neither of these writers has quite expressed the extraordinary feeling of joy and relief which we all felt after this tremendous victory. Xerxes himself was hurrying back to the Hellespont; his crippled fleet was retiring to Ionia. And this was, as young Pericles was always pointing out to me, in the main the achievement of the Athenians. They had supplied far the largest contingent to the allied fleet and it was generally admitted that the architect of victory was the Athenian Themistocles. In his estimate of this statesman Pericles seems to me to have shown both intelligence and originality. It might be regarded as natural for a boy of his age to have made a hero out of one who had won so great a victory; or again one might say that the boy could reasonably have followed his elders, Xanthippus, Aristides and others, who, being political opponents of Themistocles, tended to belittle his achievements and were again beginning to combine against him. Their usual complaints against him were that he was too clever and that in promoting his own career he was weakening the landed aristocracy and unreasonably strengthening the poorer classes. Pericles, however, was never affected by arguments deriving from envy or prejudice. He knew that it is impossible to be too clever. And as for what were considered the too extreme democratic tendencies of Themistocles, he approved of them, since he could see that, though the balance of power among existing factions might be disturbed, the total power and influence of the whole state was undoubtedly being increased by Themistocles's policies. And he considered that in a stronger and broader democracy members of his own class, if they had the ability, could exercise a more powerful and fruitful influence than before. If they lacked the ability, they were in any case unfitted for responsibility.

In the year after Salamis there were often arguments along these lines. Even Xanthippus would sometimes listen in an amused and tolerant way. He had the common fault in fathers of believing that he was by nature more intelligent than his son. "When you have an estate of your own to manage, my boy," he would say, "you will think differently." And of course such statements as these are true in the cases of those many people who are capable of constructive thought only between the ages of about fourteen and twenty-one. But Pericles had a mind of a different order. His thought was never diverted by self-interest or blunted by the apathy of convention. Even his father recognized in him something that was superior and was vaguely proud of it, though he imagined that in the course of time it would turn into something more ordinary and more easily predictable.

Soon after the battle we had returned to Athens, and I was most generously offered accommodation at Xanthippus's house near Colonus. With certain reservations (for he thought all Ionians rather apt to be "too clever") he approved of the friendship that was growing up between Pericles and me. So too did the boy's mother Agariste. Her family, of course, was even more distinguished than that of Xanthippus. Indeed, there is no family in the Greek world more famous than the Alcmaeonidae — both for good and, it may be added, for evil. Agariste was the niece of the Cleisthenes who had founded democracy in Athens. She herself had much of the intellectual and political brilliance that marked her family. Like her son, she was good rather than evil; and for Pericles, who was by far her favorite son, she confidently and rightly predicted a great future. She told me once that when she was pregnant with him she dreamed that she had given birth to a lion. It was a dream which greatly impressed Xanthippus, though Agariste, being an intelligent woman, took it only half seriously. Personally I regard dreams as being more illustrative of the character or appetites of the dreamer than indicative of the future. Agariste was determined to have a distinguished son; there was, as she soon saw, nothing remarkable about her first son, Ariphron; therefore her mind concentrated all the more fiercely on the prospect of Pericles.

I doubt whether the mind of the mother can greatly influence the human embryo. Many women, both intelligent and stupid, have desired distinguished sons and, as a rule, have been disappointed. But once a child of real ability has been born, there is no doubt that his ability may be increased by the care and enthusiasm of a brilliant and ambitious mother.

Naturally I can remember with particular vividness and pleasure those winter months in Athens when I first made the acquaintance of the city, devastated as it was, and of Athenians who later became the great friends of my adult life. And I too shared in that overwhelming feeling of elation in victory — though of course the victory had still not made Greece, and far less Athens, secure. I can still see in my mind's eye that choir of young boys singing among the ruined temples of the gods the hymn of thanksgiving and praise for Salamis.

The choir was led by young Sophocles, who was to become the great poet. He was of the same age as Pericles and
was perhaps the most beautiful boy in Athens. He had not
only beauty, but exquisite manners and a really remarkable
skill in music and dancing. His family had an estate near
that of Xanthippus and he and Pericles had been friends
from early years. I loved to watch the two boys together,
for Pericles too was beautiful, though his beauty was not,
perhaps, so strictly in accordance with the demands a sculptor might make as was the beauty of Sophocles. He had,
for instance, a curiously elongated head and was somewhat
overconscious of this. He often wore a hat when it was
unnecessary to do so, and in later years would never have a
likeness made of himself except when helmeted. This was
a point eagerly seized upon, of course, by the comic poets.
It is the only example I know of any kind of affectation or
conceit in Pericles's character. In fact, when one was speaking to him, one never noticed the shape of his head at all,
which in any case was not disagreeable. What one observed
most was an almost uncanny brilliance in his eyes. He was
not restless; indeed, there was always a certain slow dignity
in his movements. But he was capable of the most rapid
changes of expression and occasionally made a quick decisive gesture that was the more impressive for being rare.
There was a peculiar charm and variety too in his speaking voice, sometimes deeply serious, sometimes passionate,
sometimes full of laughter. He was indeed (and this may
surprise you) more ready to laugh than Sophocles, who,
with an infinite grace of manner, was still somewhat conventional in his conversation and sometimes seemed almost shocked by the quick exchanges of irony or criticism
which took place between Pericles and me. It may be that
Sophocles, with all his great qualities, lacked that analytical
facility which is so important both in a statesman and in a

philosopher. Certainly in later years he showed rather less interest than I might have expected in my own philosophical writings, and I did not meet him often except in the company of Pericles himself, to whom he remained devoted to the end. I am glad that Sophocles is still alive and still writing plays which, though less interesting to a philosopher than those of young Euripides, are still most admirable and powerful productions.

But I must not give the impression that these winter months were merely a time of triumph and of agreeable conversations with boys. It very soon became clear that the Persians were still with us. Xerxes had left Europe and his fleet too had retired to its bases in Ionia; but Mardonius, with the best part of the army, was still in Greece, evidently intending to resume the campaign in the spring, and the whole of northern Greece, down to the frontier of Attica, was on his side. So was the whole coastal area of Thrace and Chalcidice. Here one Greek town had ventured to revolt and was subdued with some difficulty. A nearby town, Olynthus, was suspected of planning revolt. We heard with horror of how the Persian governor had assembled the entire population of this town in a marsh near the city and had butchered them all — men, women and children. We knew that it was possible that the same fate might befall the population of Athens.

Danger, however, bred resolution rather than fear. When Mardonius cleverly tried to detach Athens from Sparta by offering her peace, alliance and compensation for war damage, the Athenian reply was that so long as the sun kept his course in the sky, Athens would never make peace with Persia. The reply was given by the ancient Council of the Areopagus, which at this time exercised a more than normal power in politics. This council consists, of course, of those who have held the high office of archon in Athens; but in those days the archonship was a more important office than it is now. True, seven years before Salamis there had been a reform (largely initiated by Themistocles) by which the archons were chosen by lot rather than by election or personal or family influence. But they were still chosen only from the richer classes, and of course most of the council had become members in the days before the reform. It was therefore, on the whole, a conservative body. Themistocles, as an ex-archon, was himself a member, but the majority of his colleagues were opposed to him politically. Moreover, they were, in this time of peril, able to make their views felt.

The council had not only political but religious authority. It was revered as something time-honored and almost divine; for the Athenians (as I have discovered to my cost) somehow combine a genius for invention and innovation with an almost ludicrous reverence for antiquity. At one moment they can be the freest of thinkers; at the next they will be overcome by religious or superstitious scruples. So, with the Persian army poised for invasion in the spring, the people of Athens looked for guidance to this respected and ancient collection of statesmen, who did in fact show themselves both resolute and efficient — their only defect being their mistrust of Themistocles, the most able diplomatist and the most brilliant commander in Greece. His position as the hero of Salamis was too strong to be entirely undermined, and his services were used in diplomatic missions to Sparta, where he was greatly honored and greatly suspected; for he was free in his speech and scarcely bothered to disguise his contempt for the conservatism of Spartan ways and the tyranny of Spartan institutions. In Athens, however, the commands in war went to those who in the past had been his political opponents. Aristides took command of the Athenian army and Xanthippus took over the Athenian contingent of the allied fleet. Fortunately both were able men and Xanthippus in particular made excellent use of that fleet which was the creation of Themistocles.

It is worth pointing out that at this time the behavior of the Spartan government seemed to many Athenians positively treacherous; yet in the battles that followed the Athenians loyally cooperated with the Spartans and even at sea, in spite of their much greater experience and strength, they accepted Spartan leadership. This was admirable conduct and afterwards the Athenians were rightly proud of it. Yet they remained conscious that it was not matched by anything equally high-minded and generous on the side of Sparta. In those days Spartan hegemony was almost undisputed, but it soon began to be questioned, and young Pericles was one of those who questioned it most passionately and most rationally. He had an instinctive dislike for Spartan regimentation and gracelessness; now in these years he observed evidence that the Spartans were reluctant to take any risk that was not strictly in accordance with their own interests; also that the type of training and discipline which stood them in such good stead in battle was inappropriate and indeed useless in any other connection. A Spartan abroad tends to become a savage or a charlatan.

During the months after Salamis there had been plenty of time for the Spartans and their allies to have marched out of the Peloponnese and to have taken up a defensive position on the northern and western frontiers of Attica. Instead they spent the winter and spring in building a wall across the isthmus. So, in the early summer, when Mardonius invaded Attica again, we had once more to take to the ships and retire to the safety of the islands, abandoning Athens again to the Persians. Even then, there was only one man who suggested making peace, and he was stoned to death; but in spite of this national resolution, there were bitter feelings against allies who had done nothing to help. Looking across the sea from Salamis, we could see once again the cloud of smoke over what was left of Athens, and this time Mardonius completed the ruin of the city. Among the Athenians the pro-Spartan party — still, through a kind of convention, numerous — were hard put to it to find excuses for Spartan inactivity. Others found it difficult to believe that Spartan policy was not deliberate. It was openly said that Sparta had determined that, whatever the result of the war, Athens, her nearest rival in Greece, should certainly be weakened irreparably.

Xanthippus was one of those who went with an embassy to Sparta at this time. He and his colleagues did persuade the Spartans at last to act in the interests of Greece, but the action came late and the effects of previous inaction were remembered. Still, we were glad enough when we heard that the Peloponnesian army was in Attica and that Mardonius had withdrawn to the neighborhood of Thebes, where the great plain provided the best ground for cavalry, in which he was greatly superior.

At about the same time the Greek fleet sailed for Ionia with orders to keep a watch upon and, if conditions were favorable, to attack the Persian fleet, which was then at Samos. There were all sorts of rumors, which turned out to be well founded, that not only Samos but many other Greek states in Asia were ready to revolt. I should have accompanied Xanthippus on this expedition, if at the last moment I had not been struck down by a fever.

I was still convalescing when we heard the news of the great victory at Plataea, where the Greeks, under the command of the Spartan Pausanias, had routed and destroyed the Persian army of Mardonius with his Theban,

Thessalian and Macedonian allies. In the final storming of the Persian camp the Athenians, under Aristides, had played a great part. But there is no need for me to describe this battle here. Its effects were to free the mainland of Greece from all immediate danger and also greatly to increase the prestige of Sparta; for it was the Spartans who had engaged the best Persian troops. After studying the battle I am inclined to believe that the direction of these troops was faulty and timorous; but their courage and steadfastness in the actual fighting is beyond praise.

A few days later we received news of another Greek victory in a battle that had actually been fought on the same day as that of Plataea. Over the sea at Cape Mycale, near Miletus, the Greek fleet had recovered the liberty of Ionia. The Spartan Leotychidas had been in command, but in Athens, which had supplied the far greater part of the fleet, the credit for the victory was given, naturally enough, to Pericles's father, Xanthippus. Persia had now lost control not only of the Greek mainland but also of the Aegean sea. What had appeared to be impossible had actually taken place. A few small states had beaten back the greatest empire that has ever existed.

Not unnaturally the Greeks take pride in this event, but they often misrepresent it. It is constantly said, for instance, that in those great days a united Greece, under Spartan leadership, defeated the Great King. Such a statement will not bear investigation. There was Spartan leadership indeed. Anything else would have been unthinkable. But Greece was not united. With the exception of Athens, every important state outside the Peloponnese was, sometimes unwillingly, sometimes enthusiastically, on the Persian side. In two out of the three great victories the predominant part had been played by Athenian leaders and Athenian soldiers and sailors; and even at Plataea the

Athenians had some claim to have been mainly responsible for the total rout. And now, in the moment of liberation, the divergencies between the great powers — Sparta, the official leader, and Athens, the initiator of victory — became immediately acute. The tendency of Athens was to advance and to expand; that of Sparta to retreat and to contract. This clear fact was evident to Themistocles and it was evident to the young Pericles. Most people, out of convention, did not for the time being observe it. But it is a commonplace of philosophical investigation that most people do not see what is in front of their eyes.

3

□□□□□

Athens and Her Allies

AFTER THE VICTORIES we, together with the rest of the population of Athens, began to rebuild the city. The house of Xanthippus had not received extensive damage, since up to the last moment it had been occupied by a senior Persian officer. But all the temples and nearly all the poorer houses had been totally destroyed. People naturally wished first of all to make their dwelling places habitable before the winter, though there were a certain number of oracle-mongers who attempted to influence public opinion in the direction of first undertaking the reconstruction of the religious buildings. It was at this point that Themistocles once again took the initiative and once again showed his power to make the Athenians choose greatness rather than convenience. He persuaded those who had been his political opponents as well as the rest of the people that before any other work was taken in hand the fortifications of the city must be rebuilt. Ostensibly this measure was to make Athens defensible against another Persian invasion. In fact, of course, there was no danger of such a thing in the near future. What Themistocles was really aiming at was once and for all to make Athens independent in Greece. He had correctly divined the wishes and the probable actions of Sparta and he knew that there was no time to waste. Just for the moment, after the known self-sacrifice and the splendid actions of Athens in the war, it would be difficult for Sparta to intervene. Yet there were many Spartans who were already frightened not only of the growing power and prestige but of the whole spirit of Athens — a spirit of adventure and of confident democracy. Themistocles saw things, as usual, clearly and distinctly. He had an uncanny gift of estimating the future. What was almost more remarkable was his ability to carry with him Athenians who were already committed to a pro-Spartan policy.

So the work of refortifying the city was begun, and soon enough an embassy arrived from Sparta. The envoys were polite, but attempted to be firm. It was unnecessary, they said, for Athens to be fortified. In the event of another invasion, the Athenians would be welcome in the Peloponnese behind the wall already constructed across the isthmus. And in the general national interest it was inadvisable for any city north of this point to be equipped with strong fortifications, since such a city, if it fell into Persian hands, would constitute a menace to the rest of Greece.

This message is a very fair example of Spartan hypocrisy. In fact, as we knew already, the Spartans were far from enthusiastic about carrying on the war against Persia. After the battle of Mycale, not only the great islands of Samos, Lesbos and Chios had joined the Greek League, but most of the Greek cities on the Asiatic coast had also applied for membership. But Sparta was most reluctant to commit herself. Her advice to the coastal cities was that they should take to their ships and emigrate westwards.

Themistocles, however, and many other Athenians had already seen the prospect of a brilliant future. They could imagine a naval power great enough to sweep Persia from the Aegean and to guarantee the independence not only of the islands but also of the cities on the mainland. Such expansive dreams were beyond the capacity of the Spartans, and indeed, soon after Mycale, the Spartan admiral brought back his ships to home waters. Meanwhile, on the advice of Themistocles, instructions were sent to Xanthippus to employ the Athenian contingent of the fleet in carrying on the war. These instructions together with the re-fortification of Athens were absolutely decisive events for the future, and it may be that for them Themistocles deserves even more credit than for his leadership at Salamis.

The story of the fortifications is well known. We all worked at them — men, women and children — and the evidence of our hurry is to be seen to this day. We used any material that came to hand. Drums of columns were somehow incorporated into the walls, which, though not so beautifully built as the later walls around Piraeus, are still strong enough. Meanwhile Themistocles was at Sparta, protracting negotiations. When he heard that the walls were sufficiently high to be defended, he spoke out openly. Athens, he said, had the right and had shown the ability to think and to act for herself. She proposed to do so in future. A strong Athens, he pointed out, as had been shown in recent years, meant a strong Greece.

The Spartans, wholly outmaneuvered, had to dissemble their feelings; but they never forgave Themistocles and later were instrumental in his ruin. But at Athens, at least for a short time, Themistocles was as popular as he had been after Salamis. He set to work immediately and with tremendous enthusiasm on his project of fortifying Piraeus. Indeed, it was said that if he could have had his own way he would have abandoned Athens altogether, the time-honored sanctuaries of the gods and all, and would have founded at Piraeus a new city on the sea, where, in his opinion, lay the greatness of Athens and her future.

And in the next few years the naval policy which Themistocles had initiated was supported to a large degree even by his enemies and even by the pro-Spartan party. Late in the year, after the fortifications were finished, Xanthippus returned with the Athenian fleet. It was a spectacular and a symbolic occasion, for Xanthippus brought with him the great cables of flax and of papyrus which had been used for the making of the bridge over the Hellespont by which Xerxes's army had marched into Europe. These cables were dedicated by the Athenians to the god in Delphi after they had been for some time exhibited in Athens. It seemed to us that Athens had removed the chains by which Persia had attempted to fetter Europe to herself.

Both among the people and in the fleet there was enthusiasm for carrying on the war, with or without Spartan command or cooperation. Xanthippus told us how, after the battle of Mycale, he had sailed to the Hellespont and invested the city of Sestos, which was occupied by a Persian garrison. It had been a hard and long-drawn-out siege, but in the end the city had been taken and the Persian governor with many of his troops captured. Xanthippus used to relate with a kind of satisfaction how Artayctes, the Persian governor, had offered him a huge sum of money to spare his life and that of his son and how he had refused the offer. Instead he had taken Artayctes to a height overlooking the place where Xerxes had constructed the bridge. There he had nailed him to a board and, during the time when he was slowly dying, had had his son stoned to death before his eyes. Pericles, I remember, would listen with respect and a kind of professional interest to Xanthippus's accounts of the siege; but he found it difficult, I could see, to dissemble his disgust at this example of savagery. I think his feelings were shared by the most trusted and most brilliant among Xanthippus's subordinates, Kimon, whom I first met at about this time.

Kimon, of course, was the son of the victor of Marathon, the Miltiades whom Xanthippus had prosecuted more than ten years previously, who, unable to pay the enormous fine that had been imposed on him, died in prison soon after the trial, when Kimon was a boy of about eighteen. For some years he had lived in great poverty with his sister Elpinice. People used to say that his relationship with her was incestuous; but I am not prepared to assert the truth of this rumor, though certainly Kimon was always extraordinarily fond of women and certainly Elpinice was all through her life devoted to him. Though she had no dowry, she married the richest man in Athens, who not only paid off the debt owed by Kimon's father but set Kimon himself financially on his feet. From that time Kimon enjoyed for many years a career of brilliant and uninterrupted success. People would compare him for military ability with his father and for intelligent leadership with Themistocles. And if the latter comparison does him more than justice, it is still true that he was not only a daring but a wise commander. He was also immensely popular. His generosity, his open easy manner, his care for his men, his courage and his strength made him a hero in the army and the fleet. His appearance too was striking. He was tall and had a head of thick curly hair, and though he bore himself like an Athenian gentleman there was also something which seemed charmingly irresponsible about him, something naïve or almost barbarian, possibly something inherited from his mother, who was the daughter of the Thracian king Olorus.

Kimon had distinguished himself in the battle of Salamis; indeed he distinguished himself in every battle. And in the year of Salamis he had married into the clan of the Alcmaeonidae; his wife Isodice was the niece of Pericles's mother Agariste. He was devoted to her in a quite extraordinary way. This I know from my friend and pupil, the Athenian Archelaus, a most distinguished natural scientist who will, I hope, carry on my work after my death. It was Archelaus who, at the request of Kimon, composed an elegy for Isodice after her death. He tells me that Kimon was at this time quite inconsolable, and I remember pointing out to him that Pericles also was remarkable for an almost inordinate affection for one woman. Yet in all other respects, apart from physical courage, he was utterly unlike Kimon. This, as I reminded Archelaus, was an interesting example of how, in the human soul as in nature generally, quite different elements, when mixed and blended in quite different ways, can, from certain aspects, produce similar appearances.

Xanthippus himself, though he had been an enemy of Kimon's father, had done all in his power to help the young man in his career. He was constantly applauding his great qualities, though even he found Kimon's pro-Spartan sentiments somewhat exaggerated. "Athens and Sparta," Kimon used to say with a rather charming enthusiasm, "are like a fine team of horses. Running together they will win every race." This, as Pericles was quick to see, was a somewhat vulgar comparison, throwing no light on anything. It was also based on a number of inaccuracies. Kimon chose (one may say either foolishly or generously) to forget the facts that Sparta had done nothing to help Athens at Marathon, had only reluctantly fought at Salamis, and had only advanced to Plataea after Athens had been twice sacked. All he could remember was the actual fighting quality shown by the Spartans in battle. Pericles used to say to me afterwards (he was, of course, too well bred to intervene in the conversation of his elders) that if Kimon's idea of a chariot team was to yoke together a racehorse with a bull, then it was surprising that he won any victories; and in fact his victories had been won with racehorses. Indeed, Kimon in the following years was forced by the logic of events rather than by any logic of his own (he was deficient in this quality) to go on winning victories with racehorses and to pursue a policy which was to have results opposite to those which he intended.

One of the determining factors in this situation was the mere existence of Themistocles. This great man's enemies were still united against him and they did indeed succeed in keeping him out of any important command. But they could only succeed by following the policies which he initiated, so that what was meant to be an opposition to his influence became, in fact, merely an extension of it. The opposition (if such a word can be used) was led by Aristides, the man they used to call "the Just." And so far as money was concerned he deserved his nickname, though whether he deserves moral credit for his financial integrity is another matter. The fact was that he was not interested in the kind of display for which money is necessary; also he found the show of rectitude very useful to him politically. In money matters, therefore, he made a kind of profession of honesty; in everything else he was as cunning as a fox. He had been quick to see how Kimon could be used as a counterpoise to Themistocles, and it was largely owing to his influence that in the year after the return of Xanthippus from Sestos the young man was appointed to the board of generals.

For more than a decade after this Kimon was always in command and nearly always victorious. An objective student of war cannot possibly put him on the same level as Themistocles, since he lacked Themistocles's ability to estimate the future and to see where he was going. But these are rare qualities. In my day they have been fully possessed only by Themistocles and by Pericles himself. And only Pericles has been able for any long period to persuade his fellow citizens to respect rather than to resent his superior intelligence. As for Kimon, he neither had nor claimed to have unusual intellectual ability. He was successful, and he was conservative — two qualities that are apt to attract the Athenians; also, unlike Themistocles, he was modest. Not that Themistocles ever showed any vulgar ostentation, but he was impatient of mediocrity and he was fully aware of his own brilliance. And in those days even the Athenians were alarmed at what seemed the illimitable extent of his ambitions. He aimed, people said, at covering the whole sea with Athenian ships. In his mind the war with Persia was already won and he was thinking in terms of expansion to the west and south and indeed to the farthest corners of every navigable sea. It was significant that one of his daughters was called Italia and another Asia.

But, while most of the noble families disliked and envied Themistocles, the Athenian people, who might have been his allies, could not keep up with the range and rapidity of his thought. In later years, led by Pericles, they were to applaud just these ideas and even had to be restrained from exaggerating them. But now the novelty of such ambition alarmed them. They were, as always, enterprising; but only in one direction. Kimon, with his simple and courageous leadership, his modesty, his friendship for

Sparta and his respect for the past, was for them, the man of the moment. When, at about this time, Themistocles paid the expenses for the production at the spring dramatic festival of a play by the aged dramatist Phrynichus on the subject of the battle of Salamis, people were offended at what appeared to be a piece of self-advertisement. Pericles, I remember, who was then about eighteen, much deplored the fact that Themistocles, whom he greatly admired, had not employed the services of Aeschylus, a much superior dramatist. I fancy, however, that Themistocles, who always had a good reason for his actions and who certainly knew that Aeschylus was a greater master of both stagecraft and poetry than Phrynichus, employed the older man because of his connection with Ionia. People still remembered the story of Phrynichus's play on the collapse of the Ionian revolt. Themistocles now wished the same author to celebrate the liberation of Ionia, and, no doubt, to suggest to the audience that it was he himself who had been responsible for it.

Certainly the timing was apposite and, whether the audience in the theater appreciated the fact or not, it was indeed the policy of Themistocles which was in these years being proved, in the hands of his enemies, triumphant. For these were the years in which Athens took over the Hellenic leadership that had previously been exercised by Sparta. It is likely, I think, that Aristides, who stole for his own purposes so many of the political plans of Themistocles, saw what was happening and aided the event. Kimon would never, even with his passionate Athenian patriotism, have voluntarily alienated Sparta. But the main factors, undoubtedly foreseen by Themistocles, were Spartan stupidity and Spartan arrogance. One might add Spartan irresolution, for it is a fact that Spartans, when placed in unfamiliar circumstances, are so little adaptable that they tend to behave almost as though they were cowards, hurrying back, if they can, to what is known and to what does not require thought.

For all these reasons the Spartans lost the leadership of the Hellenic fleet. First their officers showed no capacity whatever to deal with Greek allies other than Peloponnesians. They could scarcely affront the Athenians, who supplied the greater part of the fleet, but they treated the newly liberated Ionians as though they were slaves. Naturally these Ionians approached Aristides, asking him to take over the command instead of Sparta, and Aristides, after having pretended to a loyal reluctance, made it clear that, so long as the allies acted for themselves, he and the Athenians would support them. By this time the Spartan government at home had become alarmed, partly because their officers overseas were showing independence (Pausanias had actually adopted Persian dress and was intriguing with the Great King), partly because of the danger that some of their own men might become infected with that new spirit of democracy and enterprise which pervaded the Athenian and Ionian contingents of the fleet. After one half-hearted attempt to re-establish their authority, they withdrew their own ships and left Athens to carry on the war.

So the great Hellenic alliance under Spartan leadership came to an end. There were on both sides professions of amity, but in fact Greece was and remains split into two sides — on the one the Spartans and their allies, on the other the Athenians and theirs. Moreover, these two sides were certain to develop in contrary directions.

So the scene was set for the life of Pericles, and before his death the full struggle between incompatibilities was joined. The struggle continues.

4

□□□□□

Early Youth

XANTHIPPUS himself took little part in the affairs of the new Athenian League. He never fully recovered from the hardships endured at the siege of Sestos and he died at the time when Pericles, as a young man, had nearly completed his military training. His death left Pericles well off, though not immensely rich, and from the time when he first took over his family estates, he managed them carefully, without avarice and without slackness. He was not indifferent to money as Aristides affected to be; nor did he squander it as his young ward Alcibiades did later. He regarded it as something to be used as wisely as possible in the interests of his friends, himself and his fellow citizens, and he arranged for the management of his affairs in the most efficient way, spending less time and labor on them than anyone I have known. Though he was living a life that was free and easy enough, it was obvious that he was fitted for responsibilities infinitely greater than the superintendence of estates or the ordinary course of military service.

As he grew into manhood his charm was as great as ever

and his intelligence shone more and more brightly. There was a delightful fervor in the way he expressed himself — a kind of mixture between gravity and wit. He sang and played the lyre well, though perhaps not so well as his friend Sophocles; but in reciting Homer he seemed to show a sense of the value of words superior even to that of Sophocles himself, who was already a poet of whom people were beginning to speak with respect.

How many of that circle of friends have since been, like myself, exiled or else killed in battle! And how clearly I remember them today! There was Damon, Pericles's music teacher and one of the wittiest and most intelligent men I have ever met. He was not only a skilled musician, one capable of making any evening memorable when he could be persuaded to play and sing, but he was by nature a philosopher. His views on the theory of music were interesting enough, but these he seemed to throw out in passing; he was capable of advancing brilliant and original theories on any subject at all. Perhaps he was most enthusiastic on the subject of politics. He would carefully examine the precise meaning of the word "democracy," and as we discussed the matter we came to see that even in Athens democracy was not totally a reality. Men were still hindered by poverty from taking a full part in the affairs of the city; the great families still exercised an influence quite out of proportion to their numbers; and venerable institutions such as the Council of the Areopagus still were able to take a stand at variance with the Assembly of the people and with the people's chosen representatives.

Damon, I remember, would develop his ideas gracefully and dexterously, rather as though he were composing music. But they were taken up with an almost savage enthusiasm by others. Notable among these was Ephialtes, a young man not much older than Pericles and one who was to become for a short time Pericles's chief collaborator in politics. Indeed, there were occasions when Ephialtes, with his strange fervor and wild sincerity, seemed almost to gain an ascendancy over Pericles. He was particularly violent in his attacks on the noble families, and of course it was even easier then than it is now to produce examples of wealthy and privileged people who, because of a private feud or merely for the sake of personal gain, deliberately acted contrary to the interests of the city. Ephialtes would often prophesy that these same great families would finally succeed in destroying Themistocles, the finest statesman that Athens had ever had, and he would ridicule Kimon as a stupid and pretentious protégé of the aristocrats.

Here, as Pericles and indeed most of us were quick to see, Ephialtes was going too far. Kimon's policy may have been mistaken, but he was an honest man and a brilliant commander. Moreover, he was undeniably popular, and we used sometimes to ask Ephialtes how he could reconcile his apparent belief that the people were always right with his assertion that Kimon, the people's favorite, was always wrong. Such questions as these used to irritate Ephialtes greatly. He would call us "sophists" (he was the first, I think, to use this word as a term of contempt). Indeed, he said, the people were always right, but only in the end. There were times, such as the present, when they could be intimidated or cajoled. What was needed in politics was legislation designed to minimize the possibilities of intimidation or cajolement. And the first steps should be to deprive the Areopagus Council of all political authority and to limit the powers of the great families, including, he would add, that of Pericles. Here he would laugh, since he had the greatest admiration for Pericles and he knew that Pericles shared most of his political ideas, although he expressed them with less bitterness.

As for the bitterness and violence of Ephialtes, some people have attributed them to the fact that he came of an undistinguished family of only moderate means; and it is certainly true that people of great abilities born in low stations are apt to resent what seems to them a personal injustice. But there was none of this meanness about Ephialtes. He was never bitter in his personal relationships. Pericles was often able to help him financially and for this help he was always grateful, never resentful. Certainly if any of his political opponents had received such help, he would have described it as bribery. For himself it was sufficient that he knew for a certainty that he could not be bribed. Thus it was natural and easy for him to accept with gratitude the gifts of a friend. Had he been rich and Pericles poor, he would have expected Pericles to have behaved in the same way.

How often have I admired the fine bodies and the eager looks of these two as they wrestled together! They were not lovers. Pericles, as I have said, was, like Kimon, strangely attached to girls and women. Though his friendship for boys and men was passionate and sincere, he did not seem to feel the need for that physical intimacy which most of us desire. Sophocles was, I think, the one in our circle who was most addicted to the love of boys. I have seen him sick and shaking with desire; yet towards each object of his affections he invariably conducted himself with infinite grace, charm and consideration.

As for my own love affairs at this time, I can remember them to this day clearly enough, but it would be irrelevant to discuss them here. I should, however, say something of the contribution that I was able to make to this circle of brilliant, passionate and beautiful young men. I was a little older than most of them and I was not an Athenian citizen, although I was as interested in Athenian politics as any of them. They liked me, I know, for myself; but they valued me particularly because of my knowledge of and enthusiasm for philosophy. Indeed, at this time in Athens it was never difficult to find an audience of people eager to learn about and to discuss the theories formed and the discoveries made in Ionia during the preceding two generations. I was, I think, the first Ionian with some knowledge of these things to reside in Athens. I found that, though many people were acquainted with the works of Anaximander and Anaximenes, scarcely anyone had heard of Heracleitus of Ephesus. His doctrine is, of course, obscure. Sometimes he writes like a kind of intelligent prophet rather than as a true natural scientist. Yet his work is both original and inspiring. In the development of my own philosophy I have found it much more helpful than that of Empedocles of Sicily (who makes the extraordinary assumption that he is divine) or even that of Parmenides, expert logician as he is. At this time, however, neither Empedocles nor Parmenides had been heard of, whereas Heracleitus had written even before the battle of Marathon. It was of him in particular that these young Athenian friends of mine wished to hear. First, I think, they were impressed by the daring and vigor of his language. I could see their eyes light up when I quoted to them such sayings as "If you do not expect the unexpected, you will not find it," or "It is the opposite which is good for us," or "Strife is justice."

For hours we would discuss the meanings which the words were intended to convey and I would observe how, as a rule, each man tended to appropriate to himself the meaning which best fitted his own character. Ephialtes, for instance, would constantly quote with approval the sentence "The people must fight for its laws as for its walls," while he would wholly disregard other sayings of Heracleitus which were of an anti-democratic character. Pericles, on the other hand, would attempt to grasp the thought of Heracleitus as a whole. Indeed, though he saw everything distinctly, he saw everything within wide horizons. He was the only politician I have known who considered politics a part of a general view of life, of morals and of the universe. Nor did this generality of his thought impair the practical impact which he made. His vision of the whole gave him force and strength as he approached the detail.

I should like to believe that in these early years I was of some help to him in the finding and defining of his vision of the whole. It was in these years that I was beginning to develop my own system of philosophy, and, as I did so, I believe I influenced Pericles in several ways. Not that he accepted as proven facts any of my theories with regard to the nature of the universe. I am reluctant to accept them myself as wholly adequate. What really impressed his thought and imagination was the size of the problem, the number and extent of worlds, limited or unlimited, and the necessity of finding, or at least looking for, in this infinitive variety of apparent chaos and contradiction a principle of order and discrimination. We could not find such a principle in the writings of Heracleitus, though these writings seemed to us to be constantly verging upon the truth. We admired the view that the universe is based upon tension and opposition, but we wished to go further, and we found that beyond the point where we could understand him Heracleitus would use terms that were symbolic rather than concrete. He speaks of rivers or of fire; but in fact the universe does not consist of rivers or of fire, any more than it consists of air or water, as the early Ionian philosophers believed.

You know that I still bear the nickname that Pericles

gave me — "Old Intelligence." Even today the children of Lampsacus shout it after me in the streets. I am glad to say that they use it affectionately and, indeed, always treat me with the deference due to my years. And I on my side am fond of them. They remind me of the boys I used to know in Athens when I was young; and, if I were to be awarded any honor after my death, the honor that I should prefer would be that my anniversary be kept as a holiday for the school children of your town. This, however, is by the way. Here it is only the nickname that concerns us, and this, though it was playfully and affectionately used then as now, was and is still taken seriously.

I should be the last to boast of my discoveries and the first to admit that they are incomplete. But it is a fact that I was the first philosopher to suggest that the principle of motion, change, becoming and creation in the universe is to be found in intelligence. It is the highest thing of which we know; and it seems natural to regard the higher rather than the lower as the supreme cause. However, I shall not discuss my philosophy here. All I wish to say is that this idea of intelligence as the guiding and creative force making and maintaining world after world was an idea which made a very great impression on Pericles. And, as the theory developed, he was quick to see that this intelligence, interpenetrating what is, bringing form out of formlessness, life out of the inanimate, must be something that never rests, something always active, always advancing. Without this constant activity, not only would all life cease to exist, but all distinction; there would be no separation of the rare from the dense, the warm from the cold, the light from the dark.

Now I would suggest (indeed I know) that Pericles shared with me some such view of the world as this and that this view (or something like it) not only gave grandeur to his political utterances but actually, in a way, determined his politics. These were always dynamic, never quiescent; and I have often wondered whether he deliberately intended Athens to represent in the civilized world just that intelligence which creates and sustains the world of nature.

I think that I may also claim that it was partly owing to my influence that Pericles became one of the few statesmen of our time who was keenly interested in science and absolutely devoid of superstition. In those early days I used to do a lot of experimental work. Not that I have ever believed that the evidence of our senses is final. Such a proposition is absurd. The underlying structure of things is beyond the reach of our senses and can only be grasped, if at all, by pure thought. Nevertheless, the evidence of our senses, if properly interpreted, is always useful and can be decisive. Moreover, I can imagine that the powers of our senses may in time be increased. If, for example, it were possible to construct some instrument which would enormously magnify the power of the eye, one might be able quite definitely to prove my theory (for which indeed there is much evidence already) that the heavenly bodies are in no way divine, but are made of matter like that of the earth on which we live. And there are many quite simple experiments which are sufficient to disprove the extravagant claims made by soothsayers and diviners.

I remember one such experiment distinctly. It was some years after the time of which I have been writing, when there was particularly bitter party strife in Athens, the two parties being led by Pericles on the one hand and Thucydides, the son of Melesias, on the other. At this time Pericles's farm steward sent him the head of a one-horned ram which had been born on his estate. The head arrived at a moment when Pericles was in conversation with me and with the soothsayer Lampon, a pompous and indeed ridiculous man, for whom Pericles had no real regard, though he found him useful politically, since he had a great reputation among the superstitious masses of the Athenians and he was apt to produce oracles and prophesies which were adapted to Pericles's own interests. The stupidity of the man is shown by the fact that he himself actually believed in these prophecies to which he owed his advancement. So, on this occasion, as soon as he saw the head of the ram with one horn he leaped to his feet and, putting on the kind of incantatory voice which was intended to suggest that he was divinely inspired, announced that the omen was sent by the gods and that its meaning was that instead of there being two parties in the state there should be one. The fact that the ram had appeared on Pericles's land indicated that it would be the party led by Pericles which would survive. Pericles, of course, listened to this performance as though he were impressed by it and saw that Lampon's words were widely publicized. But he showed a much more genuine interest when I suggested that we should dissect the animal's head, and he watched me closely as I performed the operation. I was able, of course, to demonstrate that the appearance of one horn was due to natural causes. It was a somewhat complicated chain of argument which Pericles followed easily and which was wholly beyond the comprehension of Lampon, who on this occasion as on many others accused me of impiety. The fact that his prophecy came true no doubt confirmed him in his superstition. He was indeed quite a source of amusement to Pericles and me, though in public Pericles always gave the impression of treating the man seriously, just as in all his military campaigning and in public life generally he was careful to observe the conven-

tional forms of religious observance, little though he believed in their efficacy. Nor could this attitude of his be
called hypocritical. In almost any belief, he would say,
there is to be found some portion of truth and satisfaction;
and if a powerful mind will naturally reject many accepted ideas as worthless, this does not mean that for
other minds, less enlightened, these same ideas may not
be useful and even, in a sense, true.

We talked much about religion, much about science and
philosophy in those early years. But of course Pericles was
not satisfied with theory. His life was certain to be active
and he began to act early. He was often away from
Athens, serving in those expeditions which were now setting out every year, usually under the command of Kimon,
to raid Persian territory or liberate those Greek towns
which were still garrisoned by Persians, and he won a great
reputation for personal bravery and for intelligent leadership. At the age of twenty-two he made himself known to
the general public by offering to pay the expenses for the
production of four plays at the spring festival. It was a
characteristic and a significant gesture. The fact that so
young a man should volunteer for this public service impressed people with his generosity and his patriotism.
Moreover, the production itself was unusually splendid
and thoroughly deserved to win the prize.

The poet for whose chorus Pericles paid was Aeschylus,
and one of the plays he wrote for this occasion was the
famous *The Persians*. It is, as you know, a magnificent
piece of patriotic writing, and Aeschylus, of course, was a
far greater dramatist than Phrynichus, who had previously
handled the subject of Salamis. Also, in coming forward as
the financial supporter of a play on this subject, Pericles
was making clear the direction of his political sympathies,
for it is impossible to think of Salamis without thinking of

Themistocles. Aeschylus, of course, was too great a poet to write a play in which any great stress was laid on political propaganda, nor did Pericles attempt to persuade him to insert a single line for such a purpose. But Aeschylus himself had fought at Marathon and at Salamis. To him these were still the great days, and though I think he disapproved of Themistocles on personal grounds, he was too fair a man to deny his greatness. And at this moment it was fashionable to speak ill of Themistocles. His powerful enemies, including many members of Pericles's own family, had, as Ephialtes had foreseen, finally succeeded in getting rid of him. Early in the year he had been ostracized and sent into exile for a presumed period of ten years. At the time when *The Persians* was produced he was living in Argos, a state which has always been in uneasy rivalry with Sparta, and it was already being said that his presence there was causing the Spartan government considerable anxiety. He had never disguised his contempt for the Spartan way of life, and though he must have been angry enough with his enemies in Athens, he still looked forward to his return there. So, with his restless intelligence and his great diplomatic skill, he had begun to lay the basis for an alliance between Argos and Athens directed against Sparta. And at the time when *The Persians* was performed in Athens there were many Athenians who already regretted having cast their votes against him at the ostracism.

In fact, however, Themistocles's brilliant career was almost over. He had made too many enemies and too few friends in his own generation, and those ardent supporters of his in the younger generation, such as Pericles and Ephialtes, still lacked the influence and authority to make themselves felt. He had not been in Argos for more than a year before the Spartan government sent representatives to Athens accusing him of carrying on a secret correspondence with the Great King of Persia. These accusations were eagerly taken up by Kimon's party, which included most of the noble Athenian families. Indeed, it was one of the Alcmaeonidae (not a very distinguished member of the clan) who officially prosecuted Themistocles for pro-Persian activities. As I was myself in later years prosecuted on the same charge and with the same lack of evidence, I can easily feel a special sympathy for this great man who, being in exile, could not even appear in person to answer his accusers. As it was, his written answers to the so-called evidence against him were perfectly convincing; yet he forfeited sympathy by failing to adopt that attitude of humility which the ordinary Athenian likes to see in those who are brought before the democratic courts.

And at this time Kimon was at the very height of his popularity. True, his greatest victories were won later, but he never quite so fully captured the imagination of the Athenians as in the period just after the ostracism of Themistocles. It was then that he occupied the island of Skyros, enslaved the inhabitants, who were mostly pirates, and resettled the place with Athenian colonists. But what impressed his countrymen above all was that he discovered, or claimed to have discovered, on Skyros the bones of the Athenian king and hero Theseus, who according to one legend had been treacherously killed and secretly buried on the island. These bones were brought back by Kimon to Athens, where they were interred with great ceremony and enormous popular rejoicing. All sorts of oracles were produced to show that the return of the bones to Athens indicated some special favor from the gods, that the greatest period in Athenian history was about to begin, and so on. Facts, of course, appeared to support the oracle-mongers, for in these years the fleets of Athens and her allies were rapidly gaining complete control of the Aegean.

As for the bones themselves, I was unfortunately unable to submit them to a scientific investigation; they were closely guarded by state officials. But I was able to speak with one of these officials who had actually measured some of the bones and who was able to give me a description of others. I came to the conclusion that most of the bones were those of oxen, though among them there may have been some human remains. That they ever had anything to do with Theseus is difficult to believe.

I remember that when I mentioned my views on this subject to Ephialtes he was eager to have them publicized and to use them in attacking Kimon, but Pericles and I dissuaded him from such a foolish action. When the people want to believe something, nothing will stop them from believing it, at least for some time. If Ephialtes had intervened at this moment of general rejoicing, he would have lost all the popularity which he had. And I, no doubt, should have been prematurely exiled for impiety. Kimon, moreover, probably genuinely believed in his discovery. He was a patriot and no anatomist.

Certainly Kimon's popularity at this time had much to do with the final disgrace of Themistocles. Not that Kimon himself was personally vindictive. He would have been content, I think, to have left Themistocles undisturbed until his term of exile was over. But he was incapable of resisting any overtures made to him by the Spartans, and though he may not have believed in their assertion that Themistocles was in treasonable correspondence with the Great King, he had enough political sense to see that Themistocles in Argos was a real threat to Sparta and to the Spartan-Athenian alliance. So the fate of Themistocles was a foregone conclusion. The rest of the story is well known. In the end, but not for quite a few years, Themistocles, persecuted both by Athens and by Sparta, was driven to do what he had been accused of doing and had never done. He left Greece and appeared, with great dignity, I am told, as a suppliant of the Great King. He soon, it seems, adapted himself to Persian manners and even learned the language in the short space of one year. Afterwards, he became a friend and counselor of the king's. He died with more honors in Persia than he had ever received in Athens — a point which was frequently made by Ephialtes when he attacked the pro-Spartan policy of Kimon and his party.

For in these years, when Pericles was between the ages of twenty-five and thirty, Ephialtes was becoming an important figure. He was constantly prosecuting, with or without success and on charges which were sometimes valid and often absurd, members of the Council of the Areopagus. He made many enemies, but he showed a sound political intelligence; for the Athenian people were, at long last (one may say this as one looks backwards), beginning to feel their power. They were resentful of the privileged position of the Areopagus and they were beginning to become impatient with Kimon's continual references to Sparta. "The Spartans would never do this," he would say, as though that were a sufficient argument against some measure to which he was opposed; and Ephialtes often won applause by his quick ridicule of such sentences. It almost seemed that all he needed in order to become a really formidable power in the state was a certain air of respectability. This deficiency was made good when Pericles made his first speech in the Assembly, firmly aligning himself with what seemed to many to be the revolutionary policies of Ephialtes.

5

□□□□□

The Struggle for Power

I REMEMBER very well the year in which Pericles, at the age of twenty-six, made his first speech in the Assembly. Other interesting events also occurred in this year, including one of the greatest scientific importance. For this was the year when the great meteoric body fell at Goat's River. I was informed of this event soon after it had taken place and was able to inspect the celestial sphere within a week or two after its fall. It is, of course, a sight to be seen to this day and it constitutes (I would dare to say) a decisive proof for some of my theories. It is hard and metallic. In flight it was seen to be shining. It is, I believe, of the same substance as the stars and of the sun itself, which, in my view, is at least as large as the whole Peloponnese. And, unless I am much mistaken, the source of the sun's radiance is simply heat. The moon, on the other hand, owes its light to reflection from the sun. But I am digressing. All I mean to establish is that this year is one which is particularly clear in my memory.

There were other events too, not of scientific but of literary and political interest. This was the year when our friend Sophocles first won the prize at the dramatic festival. There was extremely keen feeling on the part of the audience (a feeling that is often aroused when a brilliant newcomer challenges an accepted champion), so keen indeed that the controllers of the festival invited Kimon and his nine colleagues on the board of generals to take the place of the usual judges. They awarded the prize to Sophocles rather than to Aeschylus not for any political reason, but simply out of admiration for the young man's extraordinary talent and, possibly, because they were tired of seeing Aeschylus always winning the prize. Aeschylus (though he undoubtedly considered himself the superior dramatist) took his defeat well; and indeed not even Aeschylus could be angry or offended with Sophocles, whose manners were always gracious and whose attitude towards elder poets was invariably deferential. Still, to us this victory of Sophocles seemed to mark the end of an epoch. A new clarity had appeared in the theater, just as a new clarity was appearing in the arts (Pheidias was already working) and in public speaking.

It was in this year too that Aristides died. He, now that Themistocles was in exile, had been the last of the great leaders of the resistance to the Persian invasion still active in politics, so that his death seemed also to mark some kind of turning point. Now Kimon alone stood at the head of the party of what might be called established and conservative authority, and Kimon's extravagant respect for Sparta, which Aristides had not shared, made him, in spite of his military successes and his personal popularity, vulnerable. He was still, unquestionably, supreme. But Athenians do not like people to be long so, and Ephialtes, with his evident sincerity and his quick wit, was already beginning to win some support in the Assembly at the time when Pericles first came forward to speak there.

He had taken, I remember, enormous trouble over the preparation of this first speech of his, and this in spite of the fact that he was naturally gifted for oratory. He was nervous too and, though not at all lacking in resolution, somehow lacking in confidence. He rehearsed his speech several times before me and other friends of his, taking our criticisms most seriously, although in fact there was little room for criticism. I suppose that at the time what we remarked on most was his dignity of manner; wit and brilliance we expected of him, but what surprised us was the air of authority, worn so easily by such a young man. And by every account the audience in the Assembly was as surprised and delighted as were we, his intimate friends. Never before, it was said, had so young a man been listened to with such respect. For there was nothing either irresponsible or pompous about his delivery or about his words. What he said was both wise and unexpected, and so it was with him always. He made a practice of not speaking often (Ephialtes would make five speeches to his one), and throughout his life, even at the very few times when he became unpopular, the people would hang upon his words. Perhaps this was because he said what they themselves would have wished to say, had they the intelligence required. Certainly there was a sense in which he identified himself with them — with the whole mass of them, rather than with any particular section. Yet he was not a mouthpiece or a stimulator; he was always a leader. He never took advantage of a popular mood; he created these moods and was ahead of them. Those who listened to him became amazed at their own intelligence and resolution; they seldom realized that these were his qualities, not theirs, because he was able to present them to themselves as something which they were not, though they would like to be. And so he did, in fact, transform them.

These facts are, of course, known with regard to his middle and later life, when he had an ascendancy over this difficult democracy which is quite unparalleled. What is even more remarkable is that the qualities which gave him this ascendancy were shown, and recognized, from the very beginning. As I have said, he did not speak often, and at the beginning he certainly claimed no kind of leadership. If the word "leader" can be used at all, then Ephialtes was the leader of the party and Pericles a subordinate. Yet from the beginning, by all accounts, Pericles commanded an extraordinary respect. This did not proceed from the fact that he, the leading member of one of the noblest families in Athens, had adopted a kind of revolutionary line in politics. Others from the same family had done that before. It seems rather that Pericles was admired simply for himself. He was capable of saying what was surprising in a way that made it appear obvious. He shared his superiority with his inferiors. Indeed, he loved them.

Yet for all the respect that he inspired, it might well have seemed that he and Ephialtes were speaking for a hopeless cause. Kimon's position was very strong and in nearly all of his activities it was impossible for the extreme democrats not to support him. There was, for example, the case of the island of Naxos, a powerful place with a considerable navy and a fine force of hoplites. After having been liberated from the Persians, Naxos decided that her future was secure. So she seceded from the Athenian alliance, claiming that as the original purpose of the League had already been carried out, she and the other allies had no further obligations. It was a critical moment. Had Naxos been allowed to do as she wished, other allies also would have withdrawn their contributions in ships or money to the League and the whole basis of Athenian sea power would have been destroyed. Moreover, the Naxians had a case which was not unreasonable. It was a case supported, though not overtly, by Sparta, whose government was already alarmed at the growth of Athenian influence and prestige. Kimon himself must have been aware of Spartan feeling on this subject, but for once in his life he seems to have considered the Spartans wrong. He commanded an expedition which reduced Naxos to submission and he associated himself with those who described the action of Naxos as "revolt." With this behavior of his, Ephialtes and Pericles could not quarrel. They, even more than Kimon, would support an Athenian League which, from this moment, was becoming an empire. And soon afterwards Kimon won the greatest victories of his whole career when, at the River Eurymedon in southeast Asia, he destroyed in one day a large army and an enormous Persian fleet. The enemies of Kimon might claim, as Ephialtes did, that the two hundred Athenian triremes which took part in this expedition had been designed and laid down by Themistocles; but no one could dispute the fact that in these spectacular victories, in which two hundred enemy ships were captured, the daring and efficiency of Kimon himself had been decisive.

In the same year Themistocles himself, after having sought refuge in vain in many of the Greek states which had been saved by his genius, was forced to throw himself on the mercy of the Great King. It was a moment when it might well have seemed that Kimon and his party were secure in power and that the attacks made on this dominant party by Ephialtes and by Pericles were likely to be no more effective than is the barking of dogs upon an armed man. But, as I have observed elsewhere, change can be not only gradual but catastrophic. Within a few years of this, his greatest victory, Kimon was in exile and his whole policy had been reversed. His downfall was due in part to the opposition of Ephialtes and Pericles, but this opposition could never have been successful had it not been for the jealous and shortsighted policy of Sparta, the state which Kimon himself revered most of all.

The Athenians, like most men, worship success, but they would have forgiven Kimon almost any failure except one that concerned Sparta and their own pride. And as it was, there were some military failures in the years that followed the victories of the Eurymedon. There was, I remember, at this time much discussion as to how the forces of the League were to be employed now that Persian naval power had been so thoroughly shattered. Some were in favor of going on to liberate Cyprus, and this would indeed have been a patriotic action in accordance with the declared policy of the League. In fact, however, these forces were used more simply in the interests of Athens, and once again there was dissension within the League. Athens already controlled the sea routes into the Black Sea; she now wished to control also the land route by which Xerxes had marched, and at the same time to secure a hold over the gold mines of Thrace and the very profitable trade with the interior. It was one of those plans which are dear to the Athenians, for the possibilities seemed almost limitless. And the plan seemed to be well made. First a colony was to be established on the River Strymon at Nine Ways (the place now called Amphipolis), and from this excellent strategic position Athenian power and influence were to be extended through Thrace and Macedonia. It was a plan with which neither Ephialtes nor Pericles found any fault.

Yet the plan miscarried. In the first place it was opposed by the people of Thasos, which at that time was a rich and powerful island contributing a large fleet, manned by her own citizens, to the Athenian alliance. Thasos was the second ally to secede from the League, and Kimon was forced to divert part of his powerful force to deal with what was now generally described as a "revolt." And the Thasians acted with skill and resolution. Their fleet was, as might have been expected, driven from the sea, but not before it had sunk thirty-three Athenian warships. This was the greatest, indeed almost the only, loss that Athens had suffered since Salamis, and even after their naval defeat the Thasians did not surrender. They had good fortifications and had taken steps to equip themselves for a long siege. The Athenians reacted as they always do in such emergencies; they sent out more ships and more men; but still Kimon's original force was weakened, and though the colonists were safely established at Nine Ways, their military strength was less than it should have been.

But what was of the greatest importance for the future was this: the people of Thasos appealed to Sparta and, for the first time, described Athens as "the tyrant city." The purpose of the League, they claimed, was to liberate the Greeks. In fact it was being employed to enslave them. And they called upon Sparta, as the acknowledged leader of the Greek world, to intervene in the cause of liberty. A strange request indeed, my friends! Not that liberty is unimportant; only that it is a word capable of a great variety of meanings. Today, for example, both Athens and Sparta claim to be fighting for liberty; yet both cannot be fighting for the same thing, and it is not impossible that the final result of the struggle will be to deprive each state of the liberty which it now possesses. But what is really remarkable about the appeal of the Thasians and about the later appeals which led to the present war is that anyone should have thought that Sparta could be conceivably interested in any kind of liberty whatever. We have here, I think, to consider a complete misuse of words, a misuse common enough in politics, yet one which would be absolutely fatal to any philosophical or historical investigation. What distinguished my friend Pericles from all other statesmen was his extreme reluctance to misuse words. He knew with perfect clarity the difference between Spartan and Athenian "liberty" — the one negative and defensive, the other positive and, within limits, aggressive. He knew that the Athenian, in his own country, was the freest man that has existed in civilized history, and he claimed that even in her imperialist ventures Athens gave more than she received. And, he would say, just as the Spartan citizen had no liberty at home, so he would prove, as he had proved, intolerant and oppressive abroad. A Spartan, to use a term from my own philosophy, is without intelligence; he is not interested in a power which creates and an organization which expands.

He is, however, interested in preventing other people from developing the powers which he lacks, and, though generally reluctant to intervene in foreign affairs, will do so when he conceives that no risk will be involved. At about the time when the Thasian ambassadors reached Sparta, there arrived news which made it appear that Spartan intervention could be carried out safely. It appeared that while Kimon was advancing into Macedonia the Athenian colonists at Nine Ways had unwisely decided upon a military expedition of their own against the neighboring Thracian tribes. These tribes are capable of uniting in an emergency and they did so on this occasion. The Athenian force was surrounded and almost entirely destroyed. It was said that no less than ten thousand men had been killed.

Such a disaster seemed to the Spartan authorities one from which Athens would not soon recover. They therefore encouraged the Thasians to resist and promised to help them. It is probable that the Spartan promises were vague, but without doubt (as was discovered later) the Thasians assumed that Sparta would invade Attica in the following spring. I think it likely that they would indeed have done so if they had not been suddenly faced with a most difficult and dangerous situation in their own country.

First, there was an earthquake in Sparta. Naturally, on scientific grounds, I did my best to investigate this thoroughly, and it is my belief that this was the worst earthquake that has ever occurred on the Greek mainland within living memory. That the town of Sparta was almost entirely destroyed is not important; there neither were nor are any buildings of distinction in the place. But the loss of life was tremendous. There were at least twenty thousand casualties, and among these were a considerable number of those highly trained Spartans of the officer class on whom the whole security of the state depends. And, since Spartan power is built on the loyalty of a few and the subjection of the rest, it was not unnatural that the subjected should seize this opportunity to revolt. Soon Sparta was fighting for her life, and it was against this background that, in Athens, the final struggle between Ephialtes and Kimon began.

In the year of the earthquake both Ephialtes and Pericles had been elected to the board of generals. For Pericles this was a peculiar distinction. He was only thirty years old, and though he had served in a number of campaigns, he was much less known than Ephialtes as a speaker in the Assembly. In politics he still followed the leadership of Ephialtes, though I doubt whether he would have continued to do so for long. He was, I remember, somewhat reluctant at this time to join Ephialtes in his violent attacks on Kimon, though he was perfectly well aware that Kimon was the chief obstacle in the way of the democratic and anti-Spartan policies to which both he and Ephialtes were committed. And now, for the first time, it was possible to maintain that Kimon had been unsuccessful. Thasos, certainly, was still under blockade and in the end would be forced to surrender. But the colony at Nine Ways had been wiped out and the campaign in Macedonia had been broken off before anything had been gained from it.

Ephialtes determined to prosecute Kimon for military inefficiency and for having taken a bribe from the King of Macedonia. This seemed a daring thing to do even when done by Ephialtes, who was known to be no respecter of persons; but when people heard that Pericles was to be associated with him in the prosecution, members of Kimon's party became not only outraged but alarmed. Kimon's elderly sister Elpinice actually offended all the rules of Athenian modesty by coming alone to Pericles's house in order to beg him not to take up the case. It was an action which surprised Pericles as much as everyone else, but he treated this fierce and resolute woman with great charm. Apparently he greeted her with the words "My dear Elpinice, are you looking for a love affair at your age?" and though he refused to dissociate himself from Ephialtes, he convinced her that he neither had nor would pretend to have any personal animosity against Kimon. In many military expeditions he had served under his leadership, and though he regarded his Spartan policy as dangerous and inept, he had no doubt of his fine qualities as a general.

When the day of the trial came, Pericles behaved as he had promised. His speech was without bitterness, but was none the less forcible for that. No one, in fact, was likely to believe that Kimon had taken a bribe, but both Ephialtes, in his most emotional manner, and Pericles, with a well-ordered telling sobriety, made damaging attacks on his conduct of the campaign. In particular they claimed to have evidence that Sparta was planning to support the rebels in Thasos. Kimon hotly denied this and once again stressed his belief that the whole security of Greece depended on the

Spartan alliance. But this part of his speech fell curiously flat. On this subject the views of Ephialtes and Pericles were beginning to gain ground. It was only when Kimon began to speak of his own achievements in war and of the munificence he had shown in beautifying the city of Athens that the audience became deeply moved. He could also, at the time of the trial, boast of how he had, in the end, conquered Thasos, destroyed her fortifications, taken over her fleet, and acquired for Athens her valuable gold mines on the mainland. There were still some who deplored such treatment of an ally, but Ephialtes and Pericles were not among them. They had favored the campaign from the beginning and had hoped for even greater acquisitions than those which Kimon had made. So Kimon was acquitted, but his prestige had been diminished.

The struggle between the parties continued, and soon after Kimon's acquittal there was another debate on his Spartan policy. Sparta had been doing badly in her war with the rebels. Large areas of the country were under rebel control and almost every area was threatened by guerrilla raids. In particular the Spartans found the task of reducing rebel strongholds in the mountains quite beyond their power. In a pitched battle Spartan infantry are incomparable, but in other military operations, where a certain versatility of intelligence is required, they are ill at ease and ineffective. So now Sparta appealed to her allies for help and, in the first place, to Athens, whose troops had had much experience of seige warfare and whose military engineers were the best in Greece.

Kimon, of course, supported the Spartan appeal, but the debate on this issue was very bitter indeed. It seems that on this occasion Ephialtes spoke with an extraordinary passion and intensity. He treated with contempt all Kimon's pleas for unity in Greece and for loyalty to allies. These, he said, were abstract and, in this case, almost meaningless notions. There could be no unity between the Athenian democracy and a tyranny. The Spartan serfs were not slaves, though they were often treated worse than slaves. They were free Greeks, fighting for the same liberty the Athenians had gained when, before Marathon, they drove out the tyrants. As for loyalty, when had Sparta shown any loyalty to Athens? The allies of Athens were not slaves; they were bound to her by legal contracts which had been entered into voluntarily. But when one of these allies had broken her contract by revolt, Sparta, so far from giving help, had actually encouraged the revolt.

All this was denied by Kimon. He too, it seems, made one of the best speeches of his career, and in the end he carried the Assembly with him. Four thousand Athenian hoplites, under his own command, were sent to Sparta. And in my view this decision was taken not so much because the Athenians felt any affection or loyalty towards the Spartans, but because they were greatly flattered at being asked for help by the most powerful state in Greece. The Athenians are more devoted to honor than any other people. They looked forward to being able to say that they, with their superior experience and intelligence, had not only saved Greece in the Persian wars, but Sparta on this occasion. But most of those in the army had listened to the arguments of Ephialtes and had been impressed by them. For once Kimon was in command of a force which was not like-minded with himself.

Indeed, it seemed that the Athenian people themselves, apart from the diminishing numbers in Kimon's party, regretted their decision once the army had marched. Ephialtes and Pericles now intensified their attacks on the privileged status of the Council of the Areopagus and this time their attacks were successful. Again the debate was embittered, for though the arguments of Ephialtes and Pericles were from a democratic view unanswerable, the Athenian, as I have said, combines the most thoroughgoing modernity with a deep sense of tradition. Though it seemed right, it seemed also impious to curtail the powers of this venerable body. I remember that the poet Aeschylus felt very deeply on this subject. However, Ephialtes won the debate. The Areopagus was stripped of all political power and of all rights of moral censorship. In future its only function was to act as a supreme court in cases of homicide. In legal and constitutional matters there was now no privileged class in the state. The will of the Assembly was supreme and has remained so ever since.

Kimon, they say, was horrified when he learned of this decision, and he promised his supporters that when he returned from Sparta he would see to it that it was reversed. It is even possible that he might have done so, if he had returned, as was his habit, with a splendid victory to his credit. But he was ruined by those whom all his life he had most admired.

It appears that the soldiers of the Athenian army, once they joined forces with the Spartans, found that their allies were everything that Ephialtes had stated them to be. They admired the Spartan discipline and dexterity with weapons, but they also observed a slowness of wit and a kind of brutality which aroused their hatred and contempt. They boasted of their own political achievements and contrasted them with the dull rigid monotony of Spartan life. Many of them indeed sympathized with the rebels, who seemed to them to be more like Greeks than were their own allies and to have every justification to be fighting for their freedom.

Not unnaturally the Spartan authorities became alarmed. They are always alarmed at the slightest sign of any revolutionary spirit, and this is understandable when one considers that they are in their own country a very small minority which exists on the subjection of others far more numerous than themselves. Now they saw among them a large and efficient army of allies who, unlike Sparta's other allies, not only had no reverence for Spartan ideals but actually despised them. True, this army was commanded by a man who had shown an undeviating loyalty to Sparta and who, in spite of the fact that he was the most distinguished general in the Greek world, was perfectly willing to subordinate himself to the Spartan high command. But Spartans are as a rule neither generous themselves nor quick to accept the generosity of others. They resented Kimon's distinction, which was well advertised by his men, and they feared his popularity even though he used it to further their own interests. In the end they requested him to leave and to take his army with him. They were perfectly capable, they said, of finishing the war by themselves.

It was a gesture of almost incredible stupidity and its effects were exploited to the full in Athens by Ephialtes and Pericles. The Athenians can bear any hardship except an insult. This they find intolerable, and when suffering from such a grievance they will take measures far out of proportion to the occasion. So it happened now. The Assembly revoked the alliance with Sparta and proceeded to form new alliances with Sparta's enemies, Argos and Thessaly, states which had been either neutral or pro-Persian in the period of the invasion. It was a complete break with the past and it was not made without the bitterest personal and political antagonisms. Kimon himself, on his return, did his best to alter what had happened in his absence. He was discredited, but he was still great and still had the support of a large body of opinion which feared the adventurous policies of Ephialtes and had been shocked by his reform of the Areopagus. Indeed, party feeling at this time was more intense then I have ever known it to be in Athens. It was fortunate that the Athenians could have recourse to their device of ostracism, for, clearly, the state could not exist with such division within it. Either Kimon or Ephialtes would have to go.

There was not much doubt as to what the result would be. Kimon now suffered the same fate as Themistocles and was exiled for ten years. Ephialtes had reached the position for which he had been ambitious since his youth. He was the first man in the state, and his friend Pericles, now in his thirty-fifth year, was not far behind him.

6

□□□□□

Success

BEFORE THE END of the year Ephialtes had been assassinated. His murderer was not an Athenian and had no grievance against him, personal or political. He was a man of criminal type with a strong Boeotian accent and had only been in Athens for a few days. Quite evidently he had been hired to do the murder and it is possible that he himself did not know who were his employers. Certainly they were never discovered. It was assumed (probably correctly) that they were members of one of those political clubs or secret societies which are numerous in Athens and are usually recruited from members of the richer families who fear the prospect of the increasing power of the democracy and are themselves either unable or unwilling to express their views in the Assembly. As a rule these clubs constitute no danger whatever to the state. The members are content to hold drinking parties at which they air their grievances in private or to celebrate religious ceremonies, often of a peculiarly antiquated kind. Violent measures are sometimes, in the heat of wine, demanded, but they are never carried out. The democracy in Athens has long been secure and most of the aristocracy who possess ability are, whatever their political views, prepared to work within it. Not only Pericles, but Kimon also, was a democrat in this sense.

It was natural that the people of Athens should be outraged at the assassination of Ephialtes and should clamor for some act of vengeance. Since the murder had taken place so soon after Kimon's ostracism it was easy and convenient to connect the two events in a causal sense. For some days the partisans of Kimon went about in terror. The feeling of the people was such that if on the merest suspicion any of them had been put on trial, they would have been unlikely to secure justice. Everyone, as a matter of course, looked to Pericles as Ephialtes's successor, and many of his supporters advised him to make use of the situation in order to get rid of the most powerful of his opponents.

On this occasion, as on so many others, Pericles showed wisdom, courage, justice, moderation and patriotism. He was aware of the laws of nature and of evidence; he knew the dangers of dissension within the state; the plans which he had for the future, plans which had been concerted with Ephialtes, demanded, above all things, unity. He knew for a certainty (as indeed did everyone else who, in the heat of emotion, allowed himself to think) that Kimon was quite incapable of having instigated a political assassination. So at this time it was Pericles more than anyone else who allayed the people's fear and anger, guiding them to a right mind and to the proper use of their natural intelligence. For the Athenians are the most intelligent people in the world and they are fully aware of it. They are also volatile and passionate. Often they allow their intelligence to be blinded by sudden passions, but when this happens they are always sorry for it afterwards and bitterly blame their leaders for having acted in a manner unworthy of them. Pericles calmly, firmly and sometimes indulgently treated them as if they were even better than themselves. There were no political reprisals after the death of Ephialtes.

Pericles emerged from this crisis with the respect of his friends and the gratitude of his enemies. The state was now free of fear, resolute and ready for a new policy of incredible scope and daring. During the next six years Athens appeared always to be operating far beyond the limits of her resources and her safety. Yet Pericles was not foolhardy; he estimated risks, allowed (insofar as anyone can) for fortune, and went into danger with open eyes.

The new policy may be described as a reversal to the policy of Themistocles, though under different conditions. In internal affairs the people, whether as the Assembly, as magistrates or as jurymen in the law courts, were to be given a greater and greater share in the government and organization of the state. Athenian sea power was to be strengthened and enlarged, not only by the building of more ships and fortifications but by the acquisition of naval bases in any part of the world where they seemed useful or desirable. The Persian war was to be prosecuted with energy. And, above all, Athens was to take over from Sparta the leadership of Greece. She was already independent; she must be made first secure and then dominant. It was in this respect (and also in internal affairs) that the policy of Pericles differed radically from that of Kimon. He did not anticipate war with Sparta immediately. Sparta was still fully occupied with the revolt of her subjects. But in the interim Pericles determined that Athens should be as secure by land as she was already by sea.

During these six years Pericles was often, but not always, a member of the board of the ten generals who, in Athens, though they are under the general control of the Assembly

and have to submit to a thorough examination of their conduct during their periods of office, have almost unlimited
powers when they are engaged on a campaign and great
authority in the direction of policy. And in these years the
most spectacular victories were won not by Pericles but by
others — Myronides, for example, who as a young man had
held command in the Persian war, and Tolmides, a man of
about Pericles's own age, who in daring and impetuosity
was often compared with Kimon. But though in these
years Pericles did not play the major part in the field, it was
he who more than anyone else planned and even directed
the whole grand plan of conquest and expansion.

Here, as in every other department of life, Pericles
thought with logic and precision. The aim was the greatness
of Athens; the obstacles in the way were Persia abroad and,
in Greece, Sparta and the Peloponnesian League. At the
moment there was little to fear from Persia. Her fleets had
withdrawn from the Aegean and no one could envisage the
possibility of another invasion like that of Xerxes. In the
light of later events it may be argued that with regard to
Persia the Athenian action was too amibitious and that the
interests of the state would have been better served by
concentrating all power against the Peloponnese. But this
argument takes no account of the realities of the time. The
war with Persia was to the Athenians a prized inheritance
from their fathers. Through this war the Athenian alliance
had come into being and still, officially, existed for its
prosecution, though, as in the case of Thasos, it had already
been turned against member states. Pericles and his party
had supported the war no less ardently than had Kimon.
Moreover, there were still Greek cities to be liberated, particularly in Cyprus. The cities there were rich and prosperous. If they joined the Athenian alliance, Athens would be
strengthened in ships, manpower and wealth. No one at

the time questioned the decision to send a large battle fleet of two hundred triremes to Cyprus.

Soon a still more splendid and promising opportunity presented itself. In Lower Egypt a native prince, Inaros by name, started a revolt against the Persian government and appealed to Athens for help, promising them every sort of advantage in the country once the Persians were driven out of it. It was obvious that such advantages would be very considerable. Athenian trading posts and cities could be established on the coast and on the banks of the Nile, and since Egypt is a rich country these trading connections could be of the greatest importance to the Athenian economy. Moreover, the Persian navies consisted now almost entirely of Phoenician and Egyptian ships. With Egypt detached from Persia and allied with Athens, Athenian sea power would be irresistible in every part of the world. Prospects such as these are the lifeblood of an Athenian and there was little doubt as to how the Assembly would behave. Orders to sail to the Nile were sent to the Athenian generals of the great allied fleet operating off Cyprus, and everyone in Athens waited impatiently for news of the expected victory, for Athenians do not expect defeat.

The news was not long in coming. The allies had sailed to the mouth of the Nile, where they engaged and defeated a large Phoenician fleet, sinking or capturing fifty ships. They had then sailed up the Nile, joined forces with Inaros and fought a great battle by land. In this battle the Greek hoplites who had been landed from the ships again proved their superiority over all other types of infantry. The Persian army was routed and its commander, a brother of Xerxes, killed. The Egyptian capital of Memphis was occupied by Inaros and the Greeks. Only one center of resistance was left, the citadel of Memphis itself, a place known as the White Castle, into which the remains of the

Persian army and garrison had fled. This place was now under seige by Greek and Egyptian troops, while a large detachment of the allied fleet was sailing unopposed along the coasts of Phoenicia, burning dockyards, sinking or capturing enemy ships and making raids on towns within access of the sea. The victories seemed as great and as decisive as had been those of the Eurymedon. In Athens even the most loyal supporters of Kimon had to acknowledge that others besides their leader could show the same daring and rapidity in action. We expected to hear soon that the campaign was over and Egypt open to Athenian enterprise. We waited for six years, and when the news came it was of disaster.

However, even before the Egyptian expedition had set sail, Athens had taken up great commitments elsewhere in pursuance of the anti-Spartan policy which was peculiarly that of Ephialtes and Pericles and had been that of Themistocles. The fundamental aim of this policy was to secure Athens against any invasion by land. The city itself was already protected by its fortifications, but she could never be perfectly safe while her communications with the great port of Piraeus were vulnerable. It was on the motion of Pericles that the Athenians now began to build their famous long walls, one of five and one of three miles in length, which provided a fortified corridor between the city and the sea. Like every building operation undertaken by Pericles, the work was splendid. Anyone who sees these fortifications today will regard them as not only impregnable but magnificent. Their effect was to give Athens all the advantages of an island, and indeed Pericles used often to say that even if Athens were to lose everything by land, she would still be, with the city itself and Piraeus and the possessions overseas protected by an irresistible navy, the strongest power in Greece.

But Athens aimed not only at strengthening herself but at weakening her enemies. The alliance with Argos was already an important step in this direction. Spartan movement was impeded not only by the casualties incurred during the rebellion of the serfs but also by the presence of a hostile power on her eastern frontiers. At about this time the rebellion ended, but it did not end in a manner that was wholly satisfactory to the Spartans, who, after years of effort, had proved themselves quite incapable of subduing the rebel stronghold of Ithome in the mountains of Messenia. Both their security and their military reputation were beginning to suffer and in the end they were glad to claim victory for what was in fact a compromise. The Messenians in Ithome, fine fighting men inveterately hostile to Sparta, surrendered their stronghold on the condition that they were given a safe conduct out of the Peloponnese. In the days of Kimon no other state would have dared to receive them, but now they were welcomed by Athens and later were to be used by her in a most important capacity.

At about the same time the people of Megara seceded from the Spartan alliance and applied to Athens for protection. They were constantly the victims of attack from the neighboring state of Corinth to their south, and they were indignant that Sparta had done nothing to restrain her Corinthian allies. This appeal from the Megarians was most gratifying to Athenian pride, but what chiefly interested Pericles was that Megara enjoys enormous strategic advantages. This city has not for many years been an important power. It is shut in between Athens and Corinth. But its territory extends from the Saronic to the Corinthian Gulfs. It has seaports on each and is therefore a position from which the whole Peloponnese can be cut off from the north. Here again Pericles found it easy to persuade the people to approve his far-reaching plans. Athenian garrisons were sent at once to the ports of Nisaea on the Saronic Gulf and Pagae on the Gulf of Corinth. Long walls were constructed to link the inland city of Megara with Nisaea, thus blocking the coastal road from Corinth into Attica. At the same time fortified posts were set up to cover the longer stretch of land between Megara and Pagae in the north. And perhaps it was the occupation of Pagae which excited the Athenians more than anything else. With a base on the Gulf of Corinth they now had for the first time in history an outlet to the west, and from here their eager imaginations were quick to range far and wide. Both shores of the Corinthian Gulf were now vulnerable to their sea power; the whole Peloponnese could be safely circumnavigated; beyond the Gulf were the still semibarbarous states of northern Greece; beyond them lay Italy and Sicily; farther still were Carthage and the fabulous wealth of Spain. We Ionians may boast of having the liveliest imaginations and the quickest wits of all men, and in these respects Athens can rightly claim to be our mother city. But the Athenians have other qualities which are peculiar to themselves: if they imagine anything desirable, they will begin immediately to achieve it, and they believe that everything which they imagine can be attained.

The alliance with Megara was certain to mean war with Corinth. The Corinthians indeed were not only infuriated but astounded at the temerity of the Athenian action. They had believed that so long as the great battle fleet of the Athenian alliance was occupied in Egypt, Athens would hesitate to risk her very existence by confronting Corinthian sea power, which was still considerable. So they put to sea confidently with their whole fleet, and were as confidently defeated by the few squadrons of Athenian ships which had been left behind to guard the home waters.

Only one enemy position of any strength remained within easy distance of the land and sea frontiers of Attica. This was the island of Aegina. Its long outline and conical mountain is visible from Piraeus and all the coastline as far as Sunium. In speech after speech Pericles had referred to this island as "the eyesore of Piraeus," and there had been intermittent warfare between Aegina and Athens from the time before the Persian wars. Up to now Corinth and the other Dorian cities of the Peloponnese had given Aegina no help. She was an important trading rival of Corinth and the Corinthians hoped for a situation in which both Athens and Aegina would wear themselves out in their struggle. Now, however, Corinth and every other Peloponnesian state that could provide ships joined forces with Aegina. Athens accepted the challenge without hesitation. She had now been reinforced by contingents of allied ships, and manned still more of her own. One of the greatest sea battles that had ever been fought between Greeks took place off the Aeginetan coast. It was a battle of Ionians against Dorians. Athens was employing less than half of her available naval power against the total sea forces of her enemies. The result was absolutely decisive. The Athenians and their allies captured seventy ships, landed hoplites on the island, and proceeded to set up seige works round the city of Aegina.

Almost every man of military age was now engaged in action either in Egypt, or in the fortifying of the Megarid, or in this expedition. To many Athenians and certainly to all the enemies of Athens it seemed that exertions on this scale could not long last and could not possibly be increased. Corinth unwisely acted on this assumption and with a large land army marched against Megara. It was a campaign which appeared well thought out and certain of at least some success. Athens would either have to abandon Megara or else withdraw her army from Aegina in order to defend the still unfinished fortifications. At the first news of the invasion there was alarm in Athens itself. But there was more enthusiasm than alarm. Pericles, in one of those speeches of his which combined extreme logical clarity with the utmost emotional fervor, explained what must be done. Athens, he said, would abandon neither her gains nor her allies. This was an occasion when those thought too young to fight could show their promise and those thought too old could add one more achievement to their great record of the past. The young had heard often enough of the Persian wars; now they could see with their own eyes how their fathers fought in them. It was the time for sons to show that they were worthy of their fathers and for fathers to challenge the emulation of their sons.

I have seldom known in Athens a day of such general enthusiasm as that on which the new army, the last man-power of the state, was called up for action. It was an army consisting of boys of eighteen and nineteen and men between fifty and sixty, and there were many either above or below these age groups who contrived to find places in the ranks. The army was put under the command of the experienced general Myronides and marched immediately to join forces with the garrisons in Megara. After the army had set out there was indeed anxiety in Athens, but there was more hope than anxiety, and when the news came it was news that had been expected. Myronides had met the full force of Corinth and her allies. He had driven them from the field; they had taken up their dead and retired to Corinth; the Athenians had set up a trophy on the battle-field.

Within a fortnight came news of a still more glorious victory on this front. It seems that the Corinthian army, all men in the prime of life, had found it impossible to bear the reproaches of their elders and juniors in Corinth for having retreated from a force of Athenian boys and grand-fathers. They attempted to explain that in spite of their retreat it was they who had had the advantage in the battle; such is the ability of man to believe in what at any time he finds it convenient to believe that they may actually have convinced themselves that they were speaking the truth. They marched out again from Corinth and began to set up a trophy of their own near the place where the Athenians had already set theirs. This time their defeat was decisive. A very large section of their army was surrounded and destroyed to the last man. Since then no Corinthian army or navy has gone into action unless with the support and under the command of Spartans.

All these events had taken place within two years, and in the following year Athens had to fight again more desperately than ever to retain the position which she had won.

The Spartans are slow to move and very reluctant to undertake campaigns outside the Peloponnese. This slug-gishness of theirs is due partly to lack of imagination and partly to arrogance. They seldom see that they are in danger until the last moment, and they believe that in any military action they are certain to prove superior to their opponents. Their recent experiences during the serf revolt had not altered their habits of thought. Indeed, some Spartans are incapable of thinking except in terms of military tactics, a subject which they have learned thoroughly and by heart. Even when they do take the field they behave with extreme caution, carefully safeguarding themselves against any attack which might be of an unorthodox kind. They are only at ease when they find themselves drawn up in full line of battle against an opposing army. In such conditions they believe, not without reason, that they are irresistible.

For some time the allies of Sparta in Aegina and Cor-inth had been urging her to act. Now, at long last, her

government decided to do so. They acted in a characteristically circuitous manner. There was no declaration of war
against Athens. The pretext for bringing an army north
of the isthmus was found in a minor quarrel between two
states of central Greece, one of which, Doris, claimed to
be the motherland of the Spartans. But the army mustered
in the Peloponnese was far larger than anything that would
be required for so trivial an affair. At the news of its
preparation and its size the Athenians strengthened their
defenses in the Megarid, making it clear that they would
allow no armed force to pass through territory under their
control. The Spartans, however, had no intention of fighting
a battle in mountainous country and in a position chosen
by the Athenians. They took their army across by sea to the
northern shore of the Gulf of Corinth, quickly settled
the affairs of Doris, and then moved eastwards into the
large, well-populated territory of Boeotia, which lies along
the northern frontier of Athens. Here they enrolled more
troops and set up in the cities governments favorable to
themselves. In particular they strengthened the authority
of Thebes, the city which had collaborated with the Persians. Soon, with a greatly increased army, they were in a
position to invade Athens from the north, and if their
action was to be effective it would have to be rapid. The
long walls were nearly finished. Aegina was under close
seige and evidently could not resist much longer.

Athens acted with her customary daring and resolution.
Pericles was one of the generals in this campaign and I
have heard from him a full account of it. It was decided that
there must be no relaxation of the grip on Aegina, but
many of the troops from the Megarid were withdrawn in
order to strengthen the army on the northern front. Of
the new allies, Argos sent a thousand hoplites and Thessaly

provided a fine force of cavalry. The heavy infantry alone amounted to fourteen thousand men. It was the largest field force that Athens had ever mustered, and at the same time a squadron of fifty ships was sent to the Gulf of Corinth — a sufficient force to make it impossible for the Peloponnesians to retreat by sea.

The Athenians always prefer attack to defense. So on this occasion they were not content to guard the northern passes. They advanced into Boeotia and took up positions near the frontier town of Tanagra. Here they came in contact with the large army of the Spartans and their allies.

On the eve of the battle the generals were confronted with a difficult personal and political problem. For these last years the exiled Kimon had been living in Euboea. Now he crossed over to the mainland and, keeping his identity secret, since he wished to avoid any appearance of illegality, he sought an interview with the generals. Pericles has often described to me the mixed feelings — surprise, fear and admiration — of the Athenian generals at the sight, after so long, of the great commander with his well-known energetic bearing, his curly hair now turning gray, that expression of resolution which they had all seen already and on many occasions in Kimon's eyes when on the point of action. He had come to beg them to be allowed to fight in the ranks as a common soldier. He knew, he said, that he and his party had been often accused of sacrificing the interests of Athens to those of Sparta. Indeed, there were actually people who believed, or pretended to believe, that it was he who was behind the present Spartan invasion and that he planned to regain power with Spartan assistance and at the price of dismantling the long walls and the defenses in the Megarid. Now he wished to make it clear that he was as ready to die for Athens when she was fighting against Sparta as he had shown himself ready to die in battle after battle against the Persians.

Neither Pericles nor any other of the generals doubted Kimon's sincerity. They had never believed the malicious rumor that he had been in communication with the enemy. On the other hand there was evidence that some Athenians, possibly the same small clique of reactionaries who had organized the assassination of Ephialtes, had certainly made contact with the Spartan command and had, in all probability, made use of the name of Kimon in order to further their own plans of overthrowing the democracy. There were also political considerations. In the event of victory, Kimon's prestige would be enormously increased; in the event of defeat the generals would be accused of having illegally allowed an exile to fight in an Athenian army. They themselves might even be prosecuted for collusion with the enemy. The Athenians have naturally a great respect for law; the whole fabric of their state is sustained by it. And most Athenian generals not only respect the law but fear it. They know that the people expect, invariably, success and are apt, often unreasonably, to disgrace any commander who has failed to achieve it. In all my time at Athens I have known only two men who were not afraid of the people. One was Pericles and the other was Kimon himself.

So on this occasion the generals refused Kimon's request. Pericles was the only one who supported it. Bitterly disappointed, Kimon withdrew again into exile, though first he sent a message to his friends in the army, asking them to fight on the following day as though he were with them.

And this indeed they did. In the long battle more than a hundred of them lost their lives, and all are agreed that as a body they fought with outstanding gallantry on that day. Pericles too was one of those of whom men spoke with a kind of awe after the battle. He had, of course, already a great reputation both as a soldier and as a commander, but it seems that on this day he fought with a ferocity that astonished even those who knew him best, seeking out danger rather than guarding against it. Perhaps he had become determined to demonstrate that it was not only the friends of Kimon who could be reckless with their lives. Or perhaps his lack of caution was the result of an overmastering passion of imagination as he saw the possibility of defeating, for the first time in history, a Spartan army on land. When I used to question him afterwards, he would smile and make little of his exploits. No one in the army, he said, had taken undue risks.

The fighting went on all day and there were very heavy casualties on both sides. By late afternoon neither army could claim any advantage over the other. The issue was determined not by military prowess but by treachery. Toward evening the whole of the Thessalian cavalry deserted the Athenians and went over to the enemy. The movement was no doubt prearranged, but the Thessalians had probably delayed it in case, by too precipitate action, they might find themselves on the losing side. These Thessalians are, in comparison with the Athenians and other Ionian cities, still in a rudimentary state of political development. Their leaders and magistrates are not elected; they are simply large landowners who are used to the society of their equals and the subservience of their vassals. In this rather primitive sense they constitute an aristocracy and, being alarmed and dismayed by the wholly different spirit that is to be found in an Athenian army, they considered that both their interests and their nature were more akin to those of Sparta than those of Athens. Here they were mistaken, for the Athenians are capable of showing flexibility and understanding in their relations with others; the Spartans are astonished by the Athenians, but despise almost everyone else.

The defection of the Thessalian cavalry and their subsequent attack on the Athenian baggage train forced the Athenians to retire to new positions, and many casualties were inflicted on them and their allies during the retreat. The retreat, however, was made in good order, and though the Spartans could claim a tactical victory they did not feel strong enough to exploit it. The Athenians expected an immediate attack on the long walls or on Athens itself, so they withdrew their army to a position covering the city. But the Spartans would take no more risks. Without having attained any of the objects of their campaign, they considered that their honor was satisfied, marched quickly back through the Megarid, which was still unguarded, and dispersed to their homes.

The Athenians had, in fact, won a strategic victory, but being used to extravagant success, they regarded it as a defeat. There was a demand for further and more decisive action, and this demand was soon met. First, however, Pericles performed an act of personal generosity and political wisdom which strengthened both the resolution and the resources of the state. It was he who proposed, in this moment of emergency, that Kimon, whose friends had amply demonstrated their patriotism on the battlefield, should be recalled. He reminded his audience that his own father, Xanthippus, had been recalled from exile during the crisis of the Persian invasion. The decree was passed with very little opposition, and Kimon came back to Athens no longer as an enemy but as a friend of the new democracy. He was immediately employed in negotiations with Sparta, and the Spartans, relieved to find that it was with him rather than with Pericles that they had to deal, agreed to an ignominious treaty providing for a four months' truce. In this treaty no mention was made of Aegina, Megara or of Sparta's new allies in the north. Perhaps the Spartans imagined that Athens was exhausted and would make no move until the following spring. If so, they were profoundly mistaken. Within two months of the battle of Tanagra Myronides led the army northwards for the second time. He met the large Boeotian army at a place called the Vine Groves, not far from the scene of the first battle. His victory was complete and decisive and he followed it up with energy. He dissolved the Boeotian League, which under the leadership of Thebes had been so recently organized by the Spartans, and set up in all the cities democratic governments loyal to Athens. Nor was this the end. The people of Phocis in central Greece, who had been angered by the Spartan intervention in Doris, were also received within the Athenian alliance. So too were the eastern Locrians on the coast. Thus within three months of their defeat at Tanagra the Athenians had gained control of the whole of eastern and central Greece as far north as the Pass of Thermopylae. By the end of the year the long walls had been completed and Aegina forced to surrender. Her fleet was handed over to Athens, her fortifications were razed, and her celebrated coinage was no longer issued. She was forced to join the Athenian League and to pay an exceptionally heavy annual contribution to the treasury at Delos. It was in these ways that Athens reacted to a single defeat.

7

□□□□□

Home and Friends

DURING ALL these years, and indeed throughout the remainder of his life, Pericles was continually busy from dawn until late at night and often through the night. When he was not in command of armies and fleets, he was occupied with politics at home. For his capacity for work alone he deserves to be famous, and it remains a wonder how he and the Athenian democracy which he guided achieved so much in so short a time. Indeed, rapidity and ambition were the outstanding qualities of the period. The building of the long walls and, later, the glorious construction of the Parthenon and the Propylaea were accomplished with a speed and perfection that seemed to most Greeks, and even to the Athenians themselves, incredible. And Pericles was the author and supervisor of nearly all these grand plans. In addition, as I have said, he was often in command by land or sea, busy with the planning of new laws to transform the organization of the democracy, designing foreign policy, receiving envoys from abroad. With so much on his hands it is remarkable that he still found time for his friends or for any kind of domestic life.

He had already organized his household in a manner from which he did not deviate for the rest of his life. Here he showed the same logical precision that he showed in politics and, indeed, in every action. The organization was designed naturally to provide security but primarily to save time. Everything was in the hands of a trusted slave, Evangelos. Pericles himself, having laid down the lines on which his property was to be administered, had nothing more to do than, from time to time, inspect this servant's accounts. Unlike every other landowner, he wasted no time on speculation or on the making of unusual profits. Every year he sold to the highest bidders the whole produce of his land for lump sums. Once the sales were concluded, he was freed from all worry and from all supervision over his estates. The buyers of the yearly produce saw to that for him. Evangelos bought day by day in the market everything that was required for the household. It was an arrangement not at all to the liking of Pericles's wife or, later, his sons. They saw others who with less landed property than Pericles possessed made larger profits and lived more extravagantly. To their criticisms Pericles was wholly indifferent.

At this time, of course, his sons, Xanthippus and Paralos, were still in their infancy and he saw little of them. His marriage had been a dutiful one. His wife was a cousin of his who, since she had no brother, had inherited her father's fortune. In such cases Athenian law demands that the heiress marry her nearest male relative, the object of the provision being, of course, to keep the money in the family. So, in conformance with the law, Pericles married his cousin, who divorced Hipponikos, the husband whom she had already.

In my view this custom is not a good one and it seems to me that the succession of property could be arranged for

in some different way. I have made many observations of
the children born to parents who are close relatives, and my
conclusion is perhaps a surprising one. While it is true
that in the cases of racehorses and other animals a certain
amount of inbreeding is positively advantageous to the offspring, the same rule does not seem to apply to human beings. I admit that some of the children of these close marriages are exceptionally brilliant, but even these often have
a strange instability, while in many more cases the children
are definitely either deficient in ability or disproportionate
in the abilities which they possess. I suppose that a horse
is a less finely organized animal than a man. Not only is it
without rational intelligence, but it is incapable of using
its limbs in a constructive manner. The seeds out of
which its nature is composed are mingled in different pro-
portions from those of man and are less adapted to a variety
of combinations. Thus when the generative elements of
these animals are combined in the production of offspring
there is a smaller possibility of error. The qualities desired
are few (in a racehorse being only speed), and two closely
related creatures already distinguished for only one quality
are likely to breed successfully. But in man the combination of elements is much more subtle and obscure. A physically perfect specimen may be both morally and intellectually corrupt, and even in a good man there are bad impulses
which are kept in check either by habit or by wisdom. Even
in ordered conditions and among men of education a natural savagery is not always repressed, and in periods of revo-
lution or disaster what is cowardly, unsightly, cruel and
depraved seems to take precedence over the nobler qualities. Excellence is always a matter of effort, and no one is
capable of more than a certain amount of effort. It may
seem logical to suppose that in consanguineous marriages

the qualities of the parents (whose nature must partake of the same seeds) will be intensified in their offspring, so that, at all events, the good will counterbalance the bad, the healthy the unhealthy and so on. But as I have explained elsewhere, nature does not work by the rules of simple arithmetic. There is a much finer and more delicate organization in what is good and what is rational than in what is irrational or depraved. Two fine organizations, even if similar, will not necessarily blend together, while what is bad will always be increased by the addition of what is equally bad.

But, my friends, I find myself guilty of a digression, and in any case my views on this subject can easily be discovered in my books. I was led to make this digression by my desire to explain the fact that both of Pericles's children by his legal wife turned out most unfortunately, revealing qualities which were certainly not evident in their father or their mother (though she was not, I think, a woman of great distinction). I suppose, as you will have observed, that within a family the generative seeds are all alike. Differences of character and looks within a family can be explained by the great amount of variation in arrangement of which these seeds are capable. And I suppose too that while defects can be increased by a process of simple addition, the finer qualities are not so easily amplified or transmitted.

I mentioned these views of mine to Pericles at the time of his marriage, but he was not impressed by them. He considered it his duty both to raise children and to obey the law. Once the children had reached boyhood, he divorced his wife so that she could return to Hipponikos. I saw this wife of his only on one or two occasions and I do not think that Pericles saw much of her himself. She was scarcely fitted to intellectual conversation and in this re-

spect differed greatly from the famous Aspasia, who combined great personal charm with the highest intelligence.
But of her I shall speak later.

In spite of all his activities Pericles continued to find
time to devote to the society of his friends. He made friends
without considering either rank or wealth, and all his
friends were men of distinction. Of our original circle all
were still present except Ephialtes. Sophocles was now in
the very first rank of Athenian dramatists and many of us
preferred his work even to that of Aeschylus. He is more
capable, I think, than Aeschylus of bringing passion under
control, and this is a most important quality in a work of
art, which should embody rather than express passion. His
thought is, I know, as acute and far-ranging as that of
Aeschylus, and he expresses it with a greater economy and
precision. In a word, I believe that what is concentrated and
controlled is more effective than what is merely powerful
and majestic and diffused. Not that I would belittle Aeschylus. He was now an old man, like all who had fought at
Marathon, but so far from showing any signs of flagging
powers, he was stimulated to greater and greater efforts,
partly by the force of his own genius and partly by his
rivalry with Sophocles. For, admirable as he was in most
ways, he was not modest and found it difficult to understand how the judges at the dramatic festival could award
the first prize to anyone but himself.

I recall distinctly and with admiration the last occasion
when Aeschylus received this honor. It was in the spring of
the year of Myronides's great victories at Megara that
Aeschylus produced his Orestes trilogy, which I believe to
be the finest of all his works. His investigations into the
problems of crime and punishment and what appear to us
to be the divided and irreconcilable counsels of the gods are
profoundly moving, and there is more vivid characteriza-

tion in these plays than in any others by the same author. For this occasion, indeed, Aeschylus displayed not only the greatness of his genius but also every trick of that stagecraft for which he is famous. His references to the recent treaty with Argos were loudly applauded by the supporters of Pericles; and in the final scene his grave and balanced estimate of Athenian justice and of the sanctity of the Areopagus was received well, so tactfully did he write, by all parties. Aeschylus was a conservative and must have deplored the reform of this body, which had only just been carried out, first by Ephialtes and then by Pericles; but he accepted it in the patriotic spirit of Athenian unity, only urging his fellow citizens not to forget, in their zeal for innovation, what was good and dignified in their old tradition. This is a sentiment which nearly always appeals to the Athenian. Then, too, those who particularly admired Aeschylus for his bold innovations in costume and stage scenery were given everything that they could desire. At the first appearance of the chorus of Furies, with their streaming hair, their wild gestures and their horrifically painted faces, large sections of the audience were overwhelmed by panic and tried to fight their way out of the theater. Order was soon restored, and once these simple people had become convinced of the irrationality of their fears, they settled down with an increased pleasure to the spectacle. It was, from every point of view, a great personal triumph for Aeschylus. Shortly afterwards he went to Sicily, where his plays were enjoying a tremendous success in the Greek cities. Within a few years he died. According to the common report, his death was caused by a tortoise dropped on him from a great height by an eagle, who mistakenly believed that the poet's bald head was a rock suited for the cracking of a tortoise shell. This is not a story which I find credible. For one thing the eagle is known to be the keenest-sighted of all living things. Moreover, its talons, though powerful, are not extensive enough to retain in midair a large and spreading carapace.

After the death of Aeschylus, Sophocles became, and in the opinion of most people still is, pre-eminently the leading Athenian dramatist. I myself, very greatly as I admire Sophocles, believed even at this time that the young poet Euripides had particular qualities of his own which would allow him to equal, and in some ways excel, the other two great playwrights. In his choruses he shows the most exquisite ear for meter and for music, and his dialogue, while less stately, is more natural than that of either Aeschylus or Sophocles. Above all he is a philosopher, and it was his interest in philosophy which allowed me to make his acquaintance and to enjoy his friendship. He has few friends, since he is of a quiet and retiring disposition and, like many men who are shy, sometimes speaks too much and sometimes too little. His family had an estate on Salamis, and Euripides, I remember, had discovered a cave, beautifully situated by the sea, into which he would retire for months at a time to study and to write. He was one of the first to acquire a fine library for his personal use. He was ten years younger than Pericles and only twenty-nine years old, I think, when Aeschylus died. His first plays were produced in the following year and, like many of his plays, only received the third prize. Now, of course, he is much more popular; but even in those days he had a small but enthusiastic body of admirers. Among these were nearly all the young men who had a deep interest in philosophy, particularly in those branches of philosophy which have a practical bearing on political life.

To me it seems that philosophy, as we understand it, began in Ionia through sheer curiosity. The first question was: What is the nature of the world in which we live? Is everything made of one substance, or are there two or more? What are the principles which determine mixture, change and motion? The very asking of these questions must challenge the conventional view of things. If, for example, we find reason to conclude that the sun is a very large object composed of much the same material as the earth, we cannot at the same time believe that it is a god, still less that it is somehow dragged across the heavens by horses. It was probably in connection with these absurd stories of the mythographers that philosophy first began to exercise what may be called a political effect. Other questions soon followed. The gods are assumed to be good. How is it, then, that many of the actions recorded of them would be regarded as shameful among ourselves? Is there, indeed, any sanction other than convention or convenience for our ideas of right and wrong? Is the powerful always right?

Such questions as these were at least as disturbing to the traditional outlook as was any skepticism about the gods, and such questions were, at this time, being asked in Athens every day. Sometimes they were asked in the pure spirit of Ionian philosophy; that is to say, out of curiosity and an intense desire to discover the truth. Sometimes they were asked callously or out of self-interest. It was amusing to the young to be able to bewilder their elders with arguments that appeared irrefutable. And it was extremely useful in any kind of political debate or lawsuit to be able to set forth one's case not only with clarity and logical precision but also with an agreeable kind of modernity and daring. It was observed that Pericles himself owed a great part of his influence and reputation to the possession of just these faculties, and clever but shallow minds failed to take into account the part played by his other qualities of integrity and magnanimity.

So too with Euripides. His brilliant paradoxes, his apparent skepticism, his skill in expressing energetically both sides of a case, his evident acquaintance with every new idea won admiration and applause, but many of his admirers were blind to the fact that the chief aims of this poet were to discover truth and to improve his fellow citizens. Pericles was an admirer of Euripides, though he preferred the work of Sophocles, and I was sometimes able to bring the two men together in discussion, since for some years Euripides was a student of mine. At these conversations Euripides was somewhat tongue-tied, though he would speak eloquently on subjects connected with his art; and Pericles, of course, was interested in the theory and practice of every art. I think that, apart from his natural shyness, Euripides was somewhat alarmed by Pericles and that, though the two had much in common, Pericles was somewhat suspicious of Euripides. These attitudes are not altogether easy to explain; for both men equally admired intellectual accuracy, ingenuity and discovery; both men were devoted to the splendor of Athens. I am inclined to think that in Euripides, Pericles saw not only many of his own qualities but also a different quality, which he mistrusted. It was a quality which would appear to him an unnatural disinterestedness. And Euripides, for his part, would observe in Pericles a singleness of purpose, almost a ruthlessness, which he lacked and may, in some moods, have envied.

For Euripides, unlike Sophocles, who could act with grace and distinction in any field of activity, never played a distinguished or energetic part in public affairs. He had, of course, like other able-bodied citizens, seen some military service, but his reactions to this service, as I have discovered in many conversations with him, were most peculiar. He was not, indeed, lacking in either courage or patriotism. Like every other man, he was proud of victory and ashamed of defeat. Nor was he foolish enough to imagine (few Athenians are) that victories can be won without bloodshed and without sacrifice. Yet he looked at these necessary concomitants of war with an extraordinary distress. When he described a battle to me he would be more likely to dwell on his impression of the faces of the wounded or the dead than on the more normal themes of difficulty, danger and elation in success. That he remained an efficient soldier in spite of this abnormal sensitivity to suffering does credit, of course, to his courage. But his intellect is so powerful that he cannot feel anything strongly without investigating very minutely both the feeling and the occasion for it. And it would not be wholly unfair to suggest that he was more moved by suffering than by the situation in which suffering was involved. He was offended by the fact that suffering seems to be a necessity of nature, and there is no doubt that this attitude of his, just as much as any philosophical considerations, affected his ideas about the gods. But they also affected his views on politics. Though he admired Pericles, recognizing his supreme ability and perfect integrity, he retained in his mind some element of doubt, some slight grain of misgiving. He was inclined to wonder, I think, whether even the great aims of Pericles were worth the sacrifices that might be involved. Aeschylus all his life was proud of having fought at Marathon. Sophocles, in the flower of his beauty, had led the choir of young men celebrating the victory of Salamis. But what Euripides, as a very small boy, saw most vividly was the pall of smoke hanging in the air as the Persians burned the city. There were times, I believe, when it seemed to Euripides that the whole of life was a trap set for man by the gods.

Now with much of this attitude both Sophocles and Pericles would have sympathized. They too were most keenly aware of the suffering and injustice of the human condition. Their characters were both compassionate and profound. Pericles himself, unlike many commanders who think first of their own glory, would never risk the life of a single Athenian unless he considered the risk fully justified, and the depth of his admiration for those who fell in battle was an indication of his perfect awareness that these men had made for their city a sacrifice of supreme value. But he, like most of us, could not conceive of life without the city. In the city, he would say, there is scope for the exercise of every kind of ability and for every type of character except one, and that is the type of man who describes himself as "minding his own business." Such people seemed to him contemptible and useless because they were only half developed and incapable of further development. He would not, of course, have classed Euripides with such people. For Euripides, as a dramatist must be, was acutely concerned in the affairs of the city and was himself a glory to it. Still, I think he may have sensed in Euripides a small yet dangerous divergence from his own complete ideal, and he was suspicious of this, knowing that great results often spring from apparently insignificant beginnings. And I am inclined to believe that he was right, though it is difficult to see precisely whence this divergence sprang. Certainly Pericles would never have concurred with those conservative critics who blamed Euripides for his extreme intellectualism, his sympathy with people not of a heroic order (such as slaves or women), and his unnecessary concern to understand and to reveal their problems. Pericles himself was, as I have said, the embodiment of intellectualism; he was as compassionate as any man I have known, and to him no human problem was a matter of indifference. I think that what perplexed and disturbed him (though he may well not have been conscious of this) was a quality in Euripides which may be described as pessimism. For there are times when Euripides suggests to us that our situation is hopeless, that the world is so formed that man's aspirations can never be fulfilled, that we miss the mark more often than we hit it, that, in a word, happiness is unattainable. And often, after facing us with such conclusions, Euripides will, as it were, break off the argument and, in one of his exquisitely written choruses, soothe our feelings by transporting us into another world, a world of enchantment and extreme beauty, but one utterly remote in time and nature from our own. From our world, he wishes sometimes, it seems, to escape into something else — just as, to employ more popular examples, the worshipers of Dionysus, in their nocturnal orgies, find relief from the exigencies of reality, and the votaries of Orphic cults and other mysteries take heart in the belief that whatever their present misery they will receive certain benefits after death. But while such religious beliefs, whether true or false, are in a sense ennobling (since it is usually assumed that after death the good will do better than the bad), and while the orgies of Bacchus undoubtedly exercise in many cases a curative influence on the mind, it is difficult to see what good social or political effect can come from a mood of such utter and complete despair that the very possibility of good is rejected. All of us who possess any sensitivity have known these moods, and when we observe them in others we will, according to circumstances, either pity or deplore them. Often the circumstances which provoke such despair are tragic in the true sense; but the emotion itself is not tragic; it is a failure of nerve.

Now the political organization developed by Pericles is the noblest that has ever been devised by man. It confers the greatest benefits on its citizens and it makes on them extraordinary demands. Obviously in such a democracy, where each single man exercises power, it is necessary that each single man must be, at least to some extent, wise, good and courageous. The common charge made against the democracy of Athens is that, human nature being what it is, it is impossible for such a state of affairs to exist; and what has astonished the world is the fact that this argument has proved untrue. It remains possible, however, that such a state of affairs may not persist. Some natural calamity (earthquake or plague), defeat in war, or violent civil strife might, theoretically, fatally disturb that due balance and proportion on which every organization rests. So far, it must be owned, Athens has shown herself to an almost incredible degree invulnerable and irrepressible. To defeat she has reacted with lightning rapidity and proceeded directly to victory; internal dissensions, even such as must proceed from the clash of such powerful personalities as Pericles and Kimon, have been solved peacefully and even amicably; scarcely any greater natural calamity has fallen on any city than the plague in which Pericles himself lost his life; yet, as we can see, Athens has recovered from the plague.

When I try to find a reason for this extraordinary strength, vigor and recuperative power of the Athenian democracy, I find it partly (as Pericles would wish me to find it) in the constitution itself, but I find it also in a magnificent and to others often an irrational self-confidence. To Pericles this confidence was rational enough; its validity had been proved by experience; and he would admit, I think, that it springs from a confidence in life itself, a fervent and creative belief that man is able to transform nature, hazardous and difficult though the process may be. And, so long as men retain this belief, I can conceive of no more perfect organization of human society than that which I have seen develop in Athens. Yet no human design is so perfect as to be indestructible. As a philosopher I am compelled to admit that if ever for any reason this superb confidence in life were to be lost, the whole fabric of Periclean Athens, and with it much of what we call civilization, would collapse. For if men see no future, they are inadequately equipped to deal even with the present. In such a state people, instead of seeking responsibilities, would decline or avoid them. They would either delegate or surrender power to others, and in so doing would cripple their own natures. In such a situation we would rightly regard them as slaves or, at the best, barbarians. The organization of the city would disappear and be replaced by a great empire like that of Persia, or a half-savage autocracy like Macedonia. The functions of government would be performed either autocratically by a monarch or invisibly by a small minority of experts. For good men, if any such remained, there would be no public use. Soldiers would become either conscript or mercenary. Philosophers and poets would be friendless except in their own circles. In despair of society and the world, they would cultivate their own personalities to the exclusion of their environment. Superstition, of course, would be rife, since without hope there is no incentive to discover the reason of things. Those who acquiesced in an imposed convention would be most happy, and the most honored would be the rich and those who, by the exercise of some talent or other, were able to entertain the masses with some substitute for pleasure.

This is, I must own, a prospect almost too dreadful to contemplate; but it is my duty as a philosopher to assert that it is not inconceivable. Nor is this discussion wholly beside the point. I was led into it by attempting to explain to myself what it was in Euripides which seemed sometimes to perplex Pericles. I believe it was this — that Euripides, with all his excellent qualities, was in some deep and hidden way ready to abandon hope, and that Pericles was aware that in his ideal society there was scope for every emotion except despair. I shall now, if I may, describe some of our discussions of the ends and means of politics, discussions in which, as I have said, Euripides never played an important part.

8

■ ■ ■ ■ ■

Theories and Acts

DAMON used to say that if one broke the laws of music, one was disturbing the structure of the universe. I think that Pericles felt much the same way about democracy. He gave the word its full meaning. Power was to be exercised by literally the whole people. Thus he was not a demagogue in the sense of one who leads the majority of the poor and underprivileged against the minority of the rich and privileged. It is true that at the beginning of his career, when with Ephialtes he was attacking the Areopagus, he did sometimes find himself regarded as particularly the champion of the masses against the few, and Ephialtes himself, in his fiery speeches, often, for the sake of his own aims, inflamed the poor against the rich. The murder of Ephialtes gave Pericles an opportunity of crushing for a long time any possible opposition from those whom he knew to be his enemies. He did not take this opportunity, partly because he hated injustice and partly because he was confident in the validity of his own political theory. Believing, as he did, that every single citizen had his part to play, he wished no one to be, for any reason except cowardice or treason, incapacitated. There was no disgrace in being poor, he used to say, and nothing admirable about being rich. The only disgrace was to make no effort to escape from one's poverty or to employ one's riches unworthily.

Now the arguments against this total democracy, which Pericles not only imagined but actually brought into existence, are many and they deserve consideration. These arguments we discussed over and over again, and we found them not to be cogent.

It is often said, for instance, that government, like any other human activity, is an art. It is no more within the capacity of everybody than is the ability to write poetry. If we wish to build a temple or a ship we go to a trained architect or shipwright, not to the first man we see in the street. In the same way government is an affair for the expert; it requires not only unusual intelligence but also experience and leisure. You cannot expect an untrained soldier to lead an army, and you cannot expect a poor man, however able, to devote his abilities to public service at the expense of ruining his own business. It is therefore better that government should be entrusted to the minority who are trained by birth and experience to this difficult task and who are well enough off to make it the chief business of their lives. And it used to be said that this principle is already enshrined in the Athenian constitution. The citizen body is divided into four classes on the basis of the ownership of property. Each class used to have (and, in some ways, still has) its separate responsibility, and only the two upper classes were eligible for the important magistracies. It is admitted that past history has shown that government by the few has often led to corruption and even tryanny. But in Athens there are safeguards. Any really flagrant act of injustice would certainly be brought before the Assembly of the people. Minor irregularities must, in the nature of things, occur, since every single official cannot possibly be subject to scrutiny in all his acts and not all men in any class are always honest. However, honesty is more likely to be found among those who traditionally take pride in political achievement and honor and who have no great need to increase their fortunes at the expense of others. In any case, this trifling risk is one that must be taken. The alternative is to put government into the hands of many who, by nature and occupation, are unfitted for it. And what is of supreme importance in government, as in shipbuilding, architecture or any other skillful activity, is efficiency.

Many people meet the above argument in the following way. Most of the premises are accepted. It is admitted that a wide diffusion of power must lead to divided councils and a certain degree of inefficiency. Ideally a small committee of the best men, or even one man of extraordinary ability, might govern the affairs of a state with more justice and with greater efficiency than is possible under a democracy. In practice, however, this is not what happens. The teachings of history on this particular point are absolutely clear. It has always been found than when power is concentrated in a few hands that power is bound to corrupt. The government of so-called "experts" has never lasted more than one generation without degenerating into tyranny. In Athens the tyrant Peisistratus performed, undoubtedly, great works and, so far as we know, behaved with moderation and respect towards the citizens. But his sons behaved very differently, and their murderers, Harmodius and Aristogeiton, are still rightly honored as liberators. A man's liberty is worth more to him than anything else. No efficiency in government can compensate for its loss. In a democracy, as in everything else, there are some defects. Its procedure may be slow and cumbrous; wrong decisions may be taken under the influence of some sudden storm of emotion in which the best will not be allowed a hearing. These are faults inherent in the nature of democracy, but they are much less serious than the dangers of allowing unrestricted power to a minority. No system of government is perfect and, man being what he is, none can be. But democracy has the inestimable advantage of guaranteeing liberty, whereas all other forms of government, however efficient, will tend in the other direction. Democracy, therefore, with all its faults, is the least bad of all the systems of government so far designed by man.

This common argument would have been treated by Pericles with contempt. He regarded democracy not as a lesser evil but as a positive good, and his theory of democracy, the basis of which had been found long ago in conversation with Damon, Ephialtes and myself, continued to develop. Damon, as I have said, regarded politics almost as a branch of music. To him each citizen had something of the value of a certain note or a certain tension of the strings of the lyre. Each was important as each contributed to the melody. And I, as a natural scientist, approached the problem from the standpoint of my philosophy. I believe, as is well known, that in everything there are elements or particles of all other things; it is the force of intelligence that has given rise to quality and distinction, through the separating of and the combination of elements that would otherwise be undistinguished and indistinguishable. So that we may rightly say that this force is creative. Not that it produces something out of nothing, since there can be no nothing; but it makes quality, by which alone we judge things, out of what has no quality. With all these ideas Pericles was perfectly familiar. What he added to the abstractions of our theories was a warm, vigorous and confident humanity. He had, may we say, the highest possible opinion of everyone. And it was here chiefly that he differed from all other political theorists.

Now all civilized men must, of course, aim at the perfection of their cities. There are certain obvious essentials. A city must be able to defend itself from its enemies; it must have the resources to feed and clothe its citizens; it must have laws by which behavior is regulated; and it must be of such a kind that its citizens will take pride in it. Most theorists, in attempting to satisfy these conditions, have, on the basis of what normally exists, commended a differentiation and specialization of functions, and as a rule (though not in Sparta) this differentiation is based on the private ownership of property. In Athens for a very long time the chief magistrates came only from the richer classes, who, since they had the means to maintain horses, also formed the cavalry. The hoplite army was composed largely of the middle classes, who at this time numbered about one hundred thousand, as compared with not more than four thousand in the upper classes. The lowest class was also large, perhaps including sixty thousand, and it was on this class that the fleet depended for its rowers and steersmen.

From a military point of view there was much to be said for the system, and in this respect Pericles made no attempt to interfere with it. He would agree that in warfare some degree of specialization is necessary. It was in regard to political power and responsibility that he differed from others. For it was his belief that every single citizen (apart from the criminal and the feeble-minded) not only had the right but the duty of taking a full part in the government and organization of the state. Many reforms tending in this direction had, of course, been made before Pericles, and notably, in the period before the Persian wars, by Pericles's great-uncle, the Alcmaeonid Cleisthenes. The distinction of Pericles was in carrying out the theory of democracy to the extreme limits which appear to be possible. His originality and his extraordinary faith in human, or at least Athenian, nature is shown in his belief that every man, given the opportunity, has the capacity to do almost everything. He held with a passionate conviction that a man who is versatile and self-disciplined is not only a finer but a stronger creature than one who is merely a specialist and who accepts a discipline that is imposed.

This is not the place to describe in any detail the working of the Athenian constitution. It is well known that supreme sovereignty resides in the Assembly of the people, that the day-to-day business of administration is carried out by the council of five hundred who are chosen annually by lot, that six thousand jurymen, organized in various courts, sit throughout the year, and that there are also nearly fifteen hundred magistrates in Athens or in her possessions overseas with all sorts of duties — religious, financial and administrative. Most of these, too, are chosen by lot and retire after their year of office. The only magistrates who are elected directly and not by the luck of the lot are the ten generals. These, unlike other magistrates, can be re-elected after their year of office, though, like all other magistrates, they have to submit every detail of their conduct each year to the scrutiny either of the law courts or of a committee of the council.

The achievement of Pericles was in developing this existing system to the greatest possible extent rather than in altering it. From the time when he and Ephialtes made their successful attack on the powers of the Areopagus, there was nothing in the Athenian constitution which at all resembled oligarchy, except a certain number of individual politicians, seldom well organized, who feared the future and regretted the past. The few vestiges of privilege soon ceased to exist. On the motion of Pericles members of the third property class became entitled to stand for all magistracies, and in practice any members of the fourth class who wished to do so could also put their names forward. More important was the system designed by Pericles which provided for jurymen serving in the law courts to be paid for their services. Hitherto these courts, with their immense power over almost all operations of state, had tended to be the preserve of the rich or the moderately well-to-do, since only these could afford to spend much time away from their work. But in Pericles's view the city needed every man and every man needed the city. The introduction of pay for jurymen meant that no one was debarred by either age or poverty from this right and this duty. It was a measure which has often been criticized. Many have accused Pericles of bribing the people, particularly the lower classes, simply to make himself popular and to secure a permanent majority in the Assembly. It was a dishonest trick, it was said, to counterbalance the popularity of Kimon, who, after arranging a five-year truce with Sparta, was again becoming a force in the state. And of course Pericles was a shrewd enough politician to know that these were indeed likely results from his policy. But still, to him they were incidental. Had he wished to bribe the citizens for his own profit at the expense of the city, he would have extended the citizenship instead of restricting it, as he did some years later. And in these years he worked, on the whole, not against, but in collaboration with Kimon. Even Kimon had begun to be somewhat disillusioned with Sparta. His chief interest was still in the war with Persia, and Pericles supported him in this interest, no doubt on the understanding that in domestic affairs Kimon would at least acquiesce in his own policies. There was never at any time anything fragmentary or opportunist in the political

theory and practice of Pericles. His aims were clear to him
from the beginning and they became clearer as time went
on. What he imagined was a city in which each man would
be self-sufficient and all men interdependent. This city was
already the greatest in Greece, but its strength and value
were not in mere size. Here as everywhere beauty and
efficiency depend on proportion. A city in which every man
cannot take an active part in government and in which
every man cannot know his neighbor has, through size, lost
the quality of a city. It becomes a disorganized collection
of human beings in which liberty is impossible and energies
cannot find their proper scope.

This view is, to some extent at least, common to all
civilized Greeks. We would all agree that a city must be
organized to form a unity. But Pericles went much further
than this. He was aware of the principles of organization
in nature, in architecture, in music and in human affairs.
In our discussions of philosophy we frequently dwelt upon
the fact that it often requires only an apparently minor
alteration in structure to transform one thing into another.
So, when Kimon would argue that fundamentally Athens
and Sparta were alike, the only differences being in variations
of emphasis on elements in the political structure, Pericles
could see clearly the fallacy in the argument. To him
Athens and Sparta were utterly and irrevocably opposed.
Each was organized to produce a different type of human
being, and to Pericles there was no comparison in value between the two types. He knew from the beginning of his
career that these types were irreconcilable, and his estimate
of the needs of Athenian security necessarily influenced, or
even shaped, much of his policy. Here again his ideas developed logically and with precision. In the first place the
growth of the Athenian democracy would be impossible if
Athens were subject, as she had been in the past, to Spartan

interference. Themistocles had taken the first steps to give Athens the complete independence which she required by fortifying the city and by increasing the navy. Xanthippus, Aristides and Kimon (though Kimon scarcely realized what he was doing) had carried the process further, and by their organization and leadership of the Athenian confederacy had in a few years doubled or trebled the resources in manpower, money and shipping available to Athens. From the time when Pericles began to exercise his long predominant influence on affairs he proceeded, more consciously than any of the statesmen before him, to make Athens first invulnerable and then superior to Sparta.

By the time of which I am writing the first object was attained and the second seemed to be within reach. There were some (notably the young general Tolmides) who believed that the moment had come to challenge Sparta in the Peloponnese. Already, in the year after Tanagra, he had circumnavigated the Peloponnesian coast with a large fleet, landing troops wherever he wished. He had burned the Spartan dockyards at Gythion and had gone on to find new allies in the western islands, to demonstrate Athenian supremacy and to fortify new naval bases in the Gulf of Corinth. It was his belief that the moment had come to finish with Sparta once and for all by means of seaborne invasions combined with Argos and with the serf population of Sparta herself. Pericles could see just as well as Tolmides the possibilities of such a plan. Had he considered bloodshed necessary he would no doubt have supported it. But he was both more cautious and more confident than Tolmides. He believed, rightly, that at the moment Athens had nothing whatever to fear from Sparta, and he was confident that so long as Athens preserved her system of alliances and retained a firm grip on her allies, she would grow stronger and Sparta weaker with every year that passed. In particular he was averse to losing Athenian lives. Kimon and Tolmides used to encourage their men by reminding them of the glory of death in battle. Pericles, who was at least as aware as they of the glory in dying for one's country and who commanded equal loyalty and enthusiasm, used to say to his men, "I am commanding free men and Athenians. You know that if it depended on me, each one of you would be immortal." He had reason to believe that time and, one might almost say, history were on the side of Athens. Sparta was shrinking into herself while Athens was advancing in every direction. New alliances were made as far west as Sicily; new colonies were established at points with strategic or commercial advantages throughout the Aegean. These colonies strengthened the position of Athens abroad and gave useful and profitable employment for the surplus home population.

During this time a Persian agent was in Sparta, spending large sums of money in an attempt to bribe the authorities to invade Attica again. That Pericles's estimate of the situation was correct may be shown by the fact that the Spartans, though they took the bribes, made no move at all. They could not afford another battle like Tanagra; they feared their own subjects; and they were bewildered by Athenian enterprise.

It should be added that Pericles, like Themistocles, while ready to take risks where risks were necessary, was fully aware of the part played in affairs by what is unpredictable. It soon appeared that his comparative caution was fully justified; for while Tolmides was raiding the Peloponnese, the news arrived of an unexpected and what must have seemed to many an irreparable disaster in Egypt.

9

■■■■■

The Egyptian Disaster and
Athenian Countermeasures

SINCE THE DAYS of Kimon's victories on the Eurymedon,
Persia's sea power had appeared negligible and her land
power incapable of concentration. The very fact that the
Great King had attempted to secure the intervention of
Sparta seemed an indication of his weakness. It was natural, therefore, that when the news reached Athens that her
whole fleet and army had been destroyed, people were first
unable to believe the story and, when finally convinced of
its truth, stunned by the enormity of the disaster.

A large Persian army under a most competent commander had invaded Egypt, utterly defeated the Egyptian
rebels in battle, and then marched unopposed up the Nile
to Memphis. They had reoccupied the city and relieved
the siege, which had now lasted six years, of the White
Castle. The Athenians and their allies, with their land and
sea forces intact, had withdrawn to a defensive position on
an island in the Nile. They were prepared to stand a siege
in their turn, and though their position had certainly

worsened, it seemed by no means desperate. But they had failed to take account of the possibilities of this low-lying country with its interconnected system of waterways and canals. Before the Athenians had had time to build adequate defenses, the Persians had diverted the main current of the river. The ships were left high and dry and the army, attacked and surrounded by greatly superior forces, was cut to pieces. Only a very few had succeeded in fighting their way through, and many of them had died from thirst or exhaustion on the desert march which at length gave some of them refuge in the Greek city of Cyrene. Another Athenian force of fifty ships had sailed up one of the branches of the Nile with the intention of relieving their comrades who had been fighting so long at Memphis. They knew nothing of the battle or of the subsequent disaster or of the presence of a large Phoenician fleet, which now followed them up the river, cutting off all possibility of retreat, while both banks of the Nile were occupied by the Persian army. These ships too were destroyed or captured, and the crews and soldiers aboard were either killed or taken prisoner. So, in a few days, Athens had lost two hundred ships (a number equivalent to their whole fleet at Salamis), some thirty thousand sailors and about eight thousand heavily armed marines. It is true that more than half of these losses were from the naval and land contingents of the allies, but there was little comfort for the Athenians in this, apart from a certain diminution in the extent of merely personal loss. Already many of the allies had shown reluctance in carrying out their naval and financial commitments, and the news of their heavy losses in Egypt would certainly encourage all those who were waiting for an opportunity to secede from the alliance. In fact, within a month, news came that at Miletus the anti-Athenian party

had massacred the democratic government and proclaimed
an independent state.

In Athens the feeling was of bewilderment and of an-
guish. No comparable disaster had ever been suffered. Even
when the Persians had occupied Athens herself, the fleet
had remained intact, the losses in battle had not been
considerable, and the war had ended with Athens far
stronger than when it began. Now it appeared that the
work of years had gone for nothing. Not only power but
security was slipping away. With her diminished manpower Athens was in no position to engage once more a
Spartan army, and it seemed doubtful whether her naval
resources were strong enough to deal with any widespread
revolt among the allies. Some were for making peace on almost any terms with Sparta or with Persia or with both.
Some, as was natural, blamed the generals for their too
ambitious policies; but these were few, since ambition is
never regarded for long as a crime by the Athenians; such
malcontents also were without leadership, since Kimon had
been more committed to the Persian war than anyone
else.

The fact that at this dreadful moment the people almost unanimously looked to Pericles for reassurance and
for guidance is, I consider, one of the most notable examples of the extraordinary courage and intelligence of the
Athenians. For Pericles had already the reputation that he
was to bear for the rest of his life. It was known that he
would not speak in a manner calculated to please, that he
would not minimize difficulties, that he would be likely to
demand sacrifices and unlikely to offer easy solutions for
difficult problems. But it was also known that he would
speak with the confidence of one who has examined his
subject from every aspect and would have made up his

mind on what should be done first, what next and what last; that he would express himself with the kind of logic that would make what was confused clear; that in what he said there would be no self-interest, since his unique aim was the preservation and the glory of Athens. On such occasions the people looked up to Pericles almost as to a god, but to my mind what does them the greatest credit is that they expected from him qualities which are not always apparent in divinity. They expected to have their minds set at rest not by miracle or emotion but by the cogency of reason and the example of a consistent resolution.

Pericles did not disappoint them. He spoke with reverence and deep feeling of those who had given their lives for Athens and went on to say that unless under the most extreme compulsion it would be disgraceful to allow them to have laid down their lives in vain. Peace now was neither honorable, nor wise, nor necessary. At the moment the enemies of Athens believed her to be weaker than she was. They would therefore demand more than they had the right to have or the power to take. Athens had certainly suffered a reverse, but she was still the greatest city in Greece. She must show herself as such. Her land defenses were impregnable; her fleet, even after the losses in Egypt, was still the most powerful and experienced in the world. She had the resources and the skill to build in a few years double the number of ships that had been lost. As for the dangers of the present moment, they should be neither minimized nor exaggerated. People were inclined to think that they had most to fear from Persia and from Sparta. This view was mistaken. The Persians had been able to concentrate a large army and a powerful Phoenician fleet in Egypt. But so long as Athens held every important naval station in the Aegean, these forces could never advance farther north than Cyprus. As for Sparta, she might indeed do damage if she were to invade; but the risk involved would be a great one and Sparta had never shown herself willing to take a risk. Athens now had bases on the Gulf of Corinth and still sufficient ships to prevent a seaborne invasion, and she had defenses by land which would make any invasion by any force extremely hazardous. Moreover, Sparta had as good reasons as Athens herself to conserve her man-power. At Tanagra she had lost as many men as Athens and she had been further weakened by the earthquake and the revolt of the serfs.

The dangers immediately threatening Athens were nei-ther from Sparta nor from Persia. But there were other dangers much more considerable, and the chief of these was the possibility of disaffection among the allies. This real peril must be dealt with first. Miletus must immedi-ately be forced to submit and to punish those who had murdered the friends of Athens. There must be no relaxa-tion anywhere in the empire. New colonies should be sent out, new allies should be acquired. In the interests of greater efficiency the treasury of the League should be moved from Delos to Athens. This was, in any case, a de-sirable step to take and it could be justified in the eyes of the allies by the possibility (admittedly remote) that the Phoenician fleet might make a surprise attack on Delos.

Almost unanimously the Athenians accepted Pericles's analysis of the situation. An expedition was immediately sent out to Miletus and before long the city was forced to submit, to pay an increased tribute and to accept a gov-ernment friendly to and dependent upon Athens. At the same time Pericles himself sailed from Pagae, on the Co-rinthian Gulf, with a fleet and an army. His object was to demonstrate the existence and renewal of Athenian power and enterprise. Sailing unopposed up the Gulf, he made landings wherever he chose, enrolled more troops from allies on the southern shore, strengthened the Athenian posts in the north and advanced as far as the Corinthian colonies outside the Gulf in the northwest. All his operations were successful and were achieved almost without loss. This campaign, carried out at such a time, did more than anything else to restore Athenian confidence and to discourage those of her enemies who had believed her to be, after the Egyptian disaster, incapable of a quick recovery.

With this important object attained, Pericles now gave all his attention to the reorganization of the empire and to the rebuilding of Athenian strength. By this time the only members of the alliance who supplied ships were the large islands of Chios, Lesbos and Samos. All the rest provided money payments instead. Athenian commissioners were sent out to reassess the amounts to be paid by individual states, and in most cases the tribute was reduced. But in return for these concessions the cities were expected to make some sacrifices in the interests of the economic and military efficiency of the empire as a whole. It was in these years that the use of Athenian currency, weights and measures was introduced everywhere in the Athenian alliance. This was, quite obviously, from the point of view of the general interest, a wise step to take. But, as we all know, every city is jealous of its own individuality, and there were many who, in spite of the economic advantages to be gained, resented the loss of their own particular systems of coinage and measurement, however antiquated and unwieldy these might be shown to be. More unpopular still was the policy initiated by Pericles of planting settlements of Athenian citizens, called "shareholders," at strategic points. Tolmides established one of these colonies as occupiers of the best land on the island of Naxos. Others were placed along the vital route to the Black Sea at Andros and Euboea, and it was Pericles himself who founded the

colony across the sea from Lampsacus on the narrow straits
leading to the Propontis in the country once governed by
Kimon's father, Miltiades. Also there was more political
interference than before in the affairs of the cities. It would
be untrue to say that democratic governments were installed everywhere, but the tendency was certainly in this
direction. In most cities it was the party of the few rather
than that of the many who resented the extension of
Athenian control, and it was natural for Athens to support
her friends rather than her enemies.

Now it is chiefly with regard to these policies and others
like them that Pericles has been attacked by his enemies at
home and abroad; criticism was intensified a few years later
when he initiated the great building projects on the Acropolis and employed on these buildings, which are now, and
will remain, the wonder of the world, money contributed
by the allies to what was originally a fund for mutual defense against Persia. And at the present time, now that war
has broken out on a really great scale betweeen Athens and
Sparta, the Spartans justify their action by maintaining
that the war is for the liberation of Greece from a tyranny
imposed by Pericles on unwilling subjects.

Of course for Sparta to put forward such an argument is
plainly absurd. They have never been interested in the
liberty of anyone, except that of a small minority among
themselves, and even this minority receives an education
too narrow and too mechanical to admit of either enterprise, thought or imagination, without which the word
"liberty" is nearly meaningless. What the Spartans are
fighting for is survival.

However, because an argument is used hypocritically
it does not necessarily follow that it is untrue; and no one
who wishes, as I do, to present Pericles as he was can avoid
considering it. It is certainly an argument of which Pericles

himself understood the full force. If we attempt to follow the course of his thinking on this subject we shall find, I think, evidence of the keenest intellectual power applied with objectivity and moderation to the practical consideration of what is desirable and what is possible.

Behind everything that Pericles said and did lay his passionate and reasoned faith in the genius of the Athenian people and in the unique expression of this in the Athenian democracy. If we decide that he was, for whatever reason, mistaken in this faith, then much in his thought and action will be found to be indefensible. But I myself find it difficult not to recognize that Athens has been and still is what Pericles described it, "an education to Greece." We must first judge her by her achievements. After that it is possible to inquire whether these achievements could have been carried out by any different or better means than those employed by Pericles.

Now very briefly, and without exaggeration, it may be stated that it was Athenian enterprise and ability which were the decisive factors in winning the Persian wars and in liberating not only our cities on the Asiatic coast and on the islands but the whole of Greece. Within the Athenian democracy each man has a greater opportunity to develop each one of his abilities than exists in any other political organization. The result is a spirit of confidence, initiative and versatility which is in itself unique and which has shown itself in every field of human activity, military, political, artistic and intellectual, superior to anything else in existence. No one would question the fact that the greatest practitioners of every art and science of which we know have been either Athenians or dwellers in Athens during the present century.

This was the Athens which Pericles loved and in which he believed. But he believed in other things as well, notably in those principles of justice and moderation on which depend all structure, survival and growth. To him Athens was the best of all things. She must survive and she must grow, but both survival and growth must derive from her own nature, which, while it demanded expansion, must be regulated, like the stars themselves, by justice. Anyone who thinks of Pericles as one who sought power for its own sake or who wished to exercise a power based on the lasting subjection of others is not thinking of the Pericles whom I knew.

It is impossible, however, to deny that Pericles did employ compulsion to secure ends which he regarded as necessary, and those who adopt extreme views will say that this in itself is evidence that he failed to respect the liberties of others. Pericles himself would never accept an argument so abstracted from the real context of human existence. If all compulsion were to be regarded as an infringement of liberty and every infringement of liberty as a crime, men would have to be either above the level of the gods or below that of the beasts. Obviously, in every organization some restriction, some compulsion, is necessary. This may be regarded as a general law which is followed by everyone. Where Pericles differs from others is that the restrictions which he commended or introduced were designed not for the diminution but for the expansion of liberty.

So much for the general point of view, and let me repeat that what gave Pericles his extraordinary ascendancy was the fact that people recognized that he always, and with the utmost precision, examined the particular in the light of the general.

Certainly he believed that in the end the whole Greek world would accept the leadership of Athens and that every city would tend to imitate the Athenian constitution. This, in his view, was the best, and indeed the only, practical means of securing safety against Persia and the free development of individual life. Finally, he believed, the states would voluntarily accept such a solution, influenced by the extent of Athenian power, the brilliance of Athenian example and the clear benefits of peace and prosperity within the Greek world. At the time when Aristides and Xanthippus were organizing the original League, the cities had hurried each one to be the first to join, and in so doing they had known themselves to be acting in their own best interests. Since then the situation had not altered except in the sense that the League could employ greater strength and confer greater benefits. A state which wished to secede from it would therefore not only be weakening the whole organization but also, whether or not this were recognized, acting in a manner contrary to its own interest. The case is exactly parallel with that of a soldier who wishes to desert. Whether his motive for the wish is cowardice or some fancied personal profit, such a soldier would be glad, if he had the power of mature reflection, for the sake of his good name and his real security, to be restrained from his mistake. So Athens, in her own interest and in that of others, had the right and the duty to prevent her alliance from disintegrating.

Happiness, Pericles used to say, is impossible without freedom and freedom can be won and secured only by courage, enterprise and effort. He understood that in present conditions the freedom of Athens would always be menaced. The danger from Persia was obvious. Already the city had been twice set on fire by the Persians. So far as the war with Persia was concerned, Pericles on the whole agreed with the policies of Kimon, policies for which the League had originally been designed, though he differed from Kimon with regard to the necessary extent and duration of this war. Kimon, in his belief that this war was a great patriotic effort, would have wished it to go on without any definite limit. He even imagined the possibility of a great expedition by land and sea, under the leadership of Athens and Sparta, which would carry the war as far as Phoenicia and into the interior of Asia. The objectives of Pericles were more limited. Like Themistocles he thought first of sea power. So long as Persian sea power was neutralized and the cities and islands of the Athenian alliance were secure, he was prepared, at least for the time being, to make peace with Persia, though for the moment it was necessary to make it clear that Athens, in spite of the Egyptian disaster, was invulnerable in her own seas. And, of course, where he differed radically from Kimon was in his estimate of Sparta. He knew that Sparta looked, and would always look, at Athens with extreme fear, distrust and jealousy; this seemed to him natural and inevitable, since the whole spirit and genius of Athens were utterly opposed to the tradition of Sparta, and Sparta, by the nature of her organization, was incapable of being anything but what she was. That Athens and Sparta should cooperate in the leadership of Greece seemed to him a political, even a logical, absurdity. Certainly facts were on his side. Even at the moment of her greatest danger, Sparta had preferred to insult an Athenian army commanded by her greatest Athenian friend rather than to risk political contamination from Athenian troops. For democracy itself was a threat to the existence of Sparta, and the more successful this democracy showed itself in action, the greater the danger would be. Pericles was convinced that the Spartan and the Athenian systems could not both exist and both flourish in the same world. And since, from every point of view, he regarded the Athenian system as incomparably superior, he was determined to resist any and every attempt that Sparta might make to intervene in Athenian affairs. Probably he thought that a final trial of strength was inevitable, though he hoped that by the time the slow-moving Spartans had nerved themselves for the necessary effort, they would have been hopelessly outdistanced by Athenian speed and enterprise. With this final end in view he believed that his policies were necessary. Indeed, he would go further and say that they were not only necessary but just. Injustice, he would say, is not in the use but in the misuse of power, and Athens was the only state in history which gave to her subjects more than she received from them.

In the four or five years that followed the Egyptian disaster Sparta could, in fact, have done much damage to Athens. It was true, as Pericles had pointed out, that the defenses of Athens by land were impregnable, and that so long as her fleets remained in being she could never be decisively defeated. But both fleet and army had been seriously weakened. In my opinion (and, I think, in that of Pericles) if the Spartans had made a determined advance into the Megarid, they could have won successes which, if not conclusive, would certainly be important. Pericles, during this critical period, contrived to keep Sparta inactive, firstly by his bold initiative by sea, and secondly by giving all the support possible to Argos. There was indeed an inconclusive battle between the Spartans and an Argive army which had been reinforced by a detachment of Athenian troops. But all these operations were regarded by Pericles as preventive rather than aggressive. His fundamental concern was with the strengthening of the organization of the empire. He was ready to make peace at any time with Sparta, so long as Sparta demanded no concessions, since he knew that in peacetime the power and resources of Athens continued to grow while those of Sparta remained more or less static. He had rightly calculated that Sparta also was feeling the effect of her losses at Tanagra and would hesitate until too late to accept her present opportunity.

But Spartan pride was as powerful as Spartan caution and was peculiarly susceptible to the opinion of others. To make a peace which would recognize, overtly or tacitly, Athenian control over Aegina, the Megarid, Boeotia and both coasts of the Gulf of Corinth would be regarded by the allies of Sparta as nothing less than an abject surrender. It says much for the resolution of Pericles that in the end, with only one concession from Athens, this surrender was made. After nearly five years Kimon, who, of course, had always been in favor of peace, was able to reach an agreement with the Spartan authorities. The peace was for a limited period of five years, but Kimon hoped that in this interval a more lasting treaty would be signed. Sparta had made no territorial claims of any kind against Athens. All she gained was a cessation of Athenian raids and quiet on her eastern frontier; for Athens undertook to raise no objections to a thirty-year treaty of peace between Argos and Sparta. In Athens it was rightly believed that the settlement negotiated by Kimon was one which five years previously Sparta would have been ashamed to make, and even the most ardent supporters of friendship with Sparta were prepared to admit that in securing this great diplomatic success the resolution and daring of Pericles had played at least as great a part as the good offices of Kimon.

No sooner was the peace signed than the Athenians and their allies, again with a fleet of two hundred ships, set sail against Cyprus and Phoenicia. The expedition was under the command of Kimon. Thus quickly did Athens recover from the greatest disaster in her history.

10

□□□□□

Peace with Persia and with Sparta

FOR THIS VERY short time there was a considerable degree of cooperation between Pericles and Kimon. There was no secret of the divergence of their views about Sparta, and Pericles was more ready than Kimon to conclude an honorable and safe peace with Persia. There was a great difference in age between the two men, Pericles being now in his forty-fifth year while Kimon was nearly sixty. Nor was there any fundamental agreement on home policy. Kimon looked back to the days when every political leader except Themistocles had come from a noble family, and though Pericles certainly was no exception to this rule, his leadership, in Kimon's view, had been all in the opposite direction. However, Kimon was capable of accepting at least some facts. He realized that, contrary to his expectations, the general effect of Pericles's policies had been to strengthen rather than weaken the morale of the fighting forces, and he approved on the whole of Pericles's plans for increasing the military and economic efficiency of the empire. He had more than an uneasy suspicion that in domestic politics he was less well equipped than the younger

man, and since throughout his life his main effort and ambition had been concentrated on the war with Persia, he
was willing enough to leave home affairs to Pericles so long
as he himself was entrusted with what still seemed to him
the most important of all commands.

In the reaching of this understanding a great part was
played by Kimon's elderly sister Elpinice and by her still
more elderly husband Kallias, who was not only the richest
but one of the most respected men in Athens. He was one
of the few leading statesmen left who had fought at Marathon; he had won the chariot race at Olympia on three occasions; it had been by his money and influence that Kimon
had been rescued from poverty and given those opportuni-
ties of which he had made such brilliant use. In the past
Kallias had been, as was natural, closely associated with the
policies of Kimon and, like most of his class, opposed to
the aims and methods of Ephialtes and Pericles. But, unlike many of the rich, Kallias had a mind that was both intelligent and flexible. He saw that whether he liked them
or not, the policies of Pericles had proved amazingly successful. Like Kimon, he was in favor of peace with Sparta,
but he recognized that it was because of the resolution
which Pericles had shown that this peace had been on
terms so favorable to Athens. He was able too, I think, to
sense that Pericles, once he felt Athens to be completely
secure in the Aegean, was perfectly prepared to negotiate
a peace with Persia, and though he was aware that his
brother-in-law would oppose such a move, he was inclined
to agree with the general estimate of Pericles — that Athens,
so long as she was prepared for war, would extend her
power and influence more quickly and easily in a period of
peace.

So, while Kimon set out for the east, Pericles continued
to give his attention to the organization of the empire and

the democracy. One measure which he took at this time has aroused a certain amount of criticism from different points of view. This was his proposal to limit the citizenship to those born from Athenian parents on both sides. Some blamed Pericles for this measure on the ground that it was a step away from the long Athenian tradition of encouraging immigration to the city and making use of all human material that came to her; others accused him of irresponsible demagogy: he was once more, they said, bribing his own supporters — first he distributed lavish sums of money in state pay for the poorer classes, and now he was gaining further popularity by confirming these classes in their privileged position; others objected that this complete discrimination between the citizens of Athens and members of the alliance would lead to discontent among the allies.

It seems to me that none of these criticisms can be justified. If Pericles had wanted more supporters, he would have gained them by increasing rather than restricting the citizenship; as it was, his popularity was already great enough. Like all the measures which he took at this time, this one was determined by the needs of efficiency. It was simply a question of limiting the numbers of those eligible for state pay to the point where the machinery of government would work smoothly and economically. This pay had to come out of taxation and, in Pericles's view, the taxation of the allies was already high enough. He had no wish to restrict the influx of foreigners into Athens and would constantly refer to his pride in the fact that Athens could offer to her resident aliens more security, profit and pleasure than any other state. Athens was to lead the world not only in economic power and in all the manifestations of the intellect, but also in liberality and ease of living. He would always speak with contempt of the Spartan system of periodic deportation of aliens, contrasting it with the Athenian way of making every stranger welcome.

Most of the criticism, therefore, of this measure seems to spring from mistaken ideas about its motives and its effects. It is a fact that after it was passed more foreigners flowed into Athens, finding work and happiness there, than ever before. Indeed, the next fifteen years may be considered as the greatest age of construction that the world has ever seen. There are, I know, larger buildings in Egypt and in Babylon, but the Egyptian pyramids took several generations of men to construct and there is, so I am led to believe, something heavy and graceless in the architecture of Babylon. But Athens during these few years seemed to grow in grace and splendor every day. Not only on the Acropolis but in every quarter of the city, new buildings were to be seen in every stage of construction, new works of painting and sculpture delighted the eye. There was an endless and happy activity in which everyone in the city — citizens, foreigners and slaves — took part. And Piraeus was as busy as Athens herself. The work begun by Themistocles and continued by Kimon was being brought to completion by Pericles.

This work not only was dear to his intellect and imagination but served to give employment to every trade and art. And there was a real necessity for employment, for now came a short period of complete peace, and the city was full of soldiers and sailors released from their military duties. Kimon's long career was over and for the first time in forty years no Athenian fleet was operating against Persia. In his last campaign Kimon seems to have shown all his old skill and daring, but he was confronted by a large Persian army and Phoenician fleet under the command of the Persian general who had annihilated the Athenian force in Egypt. Kimon was able to take part in the preliminary

actions of the campaign and to give the orders which led
to its conclusion. Once more, as at the Eurymedon, the
Athenians defeated a great Persian army by land and a
great Persian fleet at sea. The action took place at Salamis
in Cyprus, but before battle was joined Kimon was dead.
For some weeks he had been prostrated by fever. Knowing
that he could not live, he gave instructions that his death
should be kept secret until the battle had been won or lost.
He may be said to have served Athens equally well by his
death and by his victory. His victory had made it clear that
Athenian power was as formidable as ever; his death removed the last obstacle to the making of peace.

The opportunity was soon taken. The fleet and army
returned to Athens with the body of the great general.
People remembered the time long ago when Kimon, in his
early and brilliant youth, had brought back (or claimed to
have brought back) the bones of Theseus from Skyros,
and now they honored him almost as a second Theseus. It
was a fine end for Kimon, though he himself would not
have approved the use to which his last victory was put.
For immediately after the funeral Kallias led an embassy
to the court of Persia and after very brief negotiations
agreed on terms for a peace which is still in operation to
this day. By this treaty Athens abandoned her claims to
Cyprus and Egypt (where indeed the Persians had already
crushed nearly all resistance), and the Great King recognized the dominant position of Athens in the Aegean. He
agreed to send no warships into what was now a sea controlled by Athens and her allies and not to move armed
forces within three days' march of the Asiatic coast. The
terms of this peace would seem to indicate that all, or very
nearly all, the aims for which the Athenian League had
first been founded had been fully attained. Persia had accepted as final her withdrawal not only from Europe but

also from the Greek seaboard of Asia and from the route to the Black Sea. It is doubtful whether Xanthippus and Aristides had ever hoped to gain so much. But even if Athenians have everything, they tend to want more, and at this time there were many of them who, in spite of the losses in Egypt, still thought that the Great King had got off lightly. Kimon, if he had lived, would certainly have been among these, and now many of his friends could be found who deplored what they described as the surrender of Greek rights in Cyprus. Some of these still held Kimon's views about the desirability of cooperation with Sparta and were aware that Pericles himself intended to use the peace with Persia to so strengthen the position of Athens in Greece that Sparta would become a secondary power. But on the whole the peace was, if not welcomed, accepted. The Athenians did not boast of it, but they were glad to have it.

With regard to the allies the problem was different and more difficult. It could be reasonably maintained that as there was now nothing to fear from Persia, there was nothing to be gained by an organization of independent states designed originally for no other purpose than to defend and liberate Greeks from Persian aggression. The allies had suffered in casualties almost as much as Athens, and those who did not provide ships and men contributed money to the alliance. It was only natural that many, particularly among the richer classes in the allied states, should think that this money could be more profitably used if diverted to their own hands. And in Athens those who opposed Pericles, either because they feared the expansive quality of the democracy, or because they had Spartan sympathies, or for both reasons at once, now appeared to have a good moral reason for withdrawal from the dangers and the hardships of continued enterprise.

These views were, as I have already explained, not tolerable to Pericles. He defended the continuance of the alliance on two grounds: first that it was necessary, and second that it was desirable in the best interests of both Athens and her allies. And, for a variety of reasons (some enlightened, some merely selfish) he received overwhelming support from all classes, and particularly from that great majority of those who had only recently become aware of the power in their possession and of the scope before them.

It was to encourage these supporters, to disarm criticism, and at the same time to give some intimation of his ultimate aims that Pericles carried through his proposal that envoys should be sent to every state in Greece to convene a Pan-Hellenic conference in Athens. This conference was to mark the end of the war with Persia, and the subjects to be discussed were the rebuilding of temples burned by the Persians, the payment of the sacrifices which in the course of the fighting had been promised to the gods, and the question of the use and freedom of the seas. It must have been clear to everyone that whatever the advantages or disadvantages in such a conference might be, Greece was being invited to confirm by agreement the exceptional position of Athens. The only considerable temples burned in the war had been those of Athens; in the war itself and in the liberation of the Greek cities far the greater part had been taken by Athens; the control of the seas was already in the hands of Athens; and as though Athens were to be acknowledged as the center and the leader of Greece, it was in Athens that the conference should meet. The proposal was, in fact, an open challenge to the established position of Sparta. In making it Pericles could claim that he was doing no more than stating the facts of the present situation. He was making clear his willingness for peace, a peace secured and guaranteed by Athenian fleets and Athenian organization. And if (as no doubt he expected) the proposal were rejected by Sparta and her allies, he would have secured at least some advantage in the fact that the rejection of such a general plan for peace and security would, in the eyes of both friends and enemies, entitle Athens to take her own steps to secure her own safety. And as it was Athens, and Athens alone, which guaranteed the safety of the allies, it was reasonable to expect the allies to continue to play their part.

So indeed it happened. The Spartans refused to have anything to do with the proposed conference and persuaded their allies in the Peloponnese to follow their example. The Athenians, on the motion of Kleinias, a member of a noble family and connected by marriage with Pericles, confirmed and strengthened their alliance, making new arrangements for the collection of the tribute. It was at this time that the cities were first required to send to Athens every four years offerings and beasts for sacrifice at the great festival of the Panathenaea, which was soon to eclipse in splendor all festivals that had ever been held in Greece.

On the whole the allies accepted the new arrangements willingly enough, though it was certainly true that in most states there were, as there are today, anti-democratic parties opposed both to their own governments and to that of Athens. These parties looked naturally to Sparta, but have never so far received any practical assistance from that quarter. The Spartans indeed spoke, as they do today, of the tyranny of Athens, but, with so large a subject population of their own, found it difficult to speak with great conviction. There have been, of course, revolts in the Athenian alliance, some of them serious, but what seems to me significant is that these revolts have nearly always occurred in isolation from each other; there has been no concerted attempt to escape from the obligations imposed by Athens. As it was, Athens a few years later had great difficulty in suppressing Samos alone, and if Samos had been joined by other states, the difficulties would have been great indeed, since Sparta would certainly have intervened. The present war would have begun much earlier and at a time when Athens was less strong than she is now. There was a strong party in Sparta which favored war, and it is certain, I think, that had there been any possibility of a general revolt in the Athenian alliance, this party would have found some pretext to break the truce and to act. That none of this happened seems to me evidence that among the allies a large majority continued to associate their own happiness and prosperity with that of Athens.

Pericles was always alive to every danger from Sparta. Here, as in other respects, his policy was consistent. He would tolerate no intervention from Sparta in anything which concerned Athens, but he preferred peace to war, being confident that peace would bring to Athens, more safely and more certainly than war, the supremacy which he had already begun to claim. And at this time he acted with more than usual caution. He was aware that the Athenian position, though secure in essentials (in the fortifications, the fleet and the alliance), was far from secure in central and northern Greece. The Thessalians had already shown themselves unreliable, and in both Megara and Boeotia, which had never been attached to Athens by any sentiment of kinship or any obvious self-interest, there were strong parties bitterly opposed to the ideas of democracy and to the infiltration of what seemed to them a foreign and dangerous way of life. Pericles believed that in time these feelings would change, but he knew that time was necessary. So he let it be known in Sparta that he was willing at any time to negotiate a lasting peace settlement to take the place of the five-year truce. But the Spartans already felt humiliated by the terms of this truce; they had lost in Kimon the only Athenian whom they trusted; and they were affronted by the claims of Athens to represent Greece. A few of them (notably one of the kings, Archidamus, who was acquainted with Pericles and respected him) were in favor of a relaxation of tension. Sparta, they argued, was a world to herself; she could always defend herself and would always be respected; foreign adventure and entanglement were contrary to Spartan tradition and dangerous to Spartan character. Such a view as this is, of course, characteristic of Spartan arrogance. And the same arrogance was expressed in the view of the majority, who demanded simply that Athens should be humbled if only by a gesture of Spartan superiority. I can see no evidence to show that anyone in Sparta had a grasp of the complexity of the whole Hellenic situation which was at all comparable with that not only of Pericles but of many other Athenians.

Before long Sparta did make the kind of gesture that seemed to be demanded. It was again characteristic that the action was taken on a religious pretext — that of restoring the administration of the sanctuary of Delphi to the citizens of Delphi. The real aim was to demonstrate Spartan authority in central Greece by proclaiming Delphi independent of the Phocians. Delphi was in the country of Phocis, but Phocis was allied with Athens. An army, rather too big for its purpose, was transported across the Gulf of Corinth, and Athens, keeping the truce, made no attempt to interfere with it. The Spartans marched to Delphi, installed their own friends in charge of the temple and sanctuary, and, on the forehead of the bronze wolf that stands in front of the temple, engraved an inscription recording their pious action and the decree passed by the men of Delphi granting precedence in the consultation of the oracle to Spartan embassies. They then marched back to the Peloponnese and dispersed.

As soon as they had gone Pericles took out a force from Athens to Delphi, replaced the Spartan-appointed guardians of the temple with the Phocians who had held the post before, and, without disturbing the Spartan inscription, had another one engraved on the side of the same wolf to record a second decree giving all rights of precedence to Athens. Spartan prestige suffered rather more than it gained as the result of this incident.

Next year, however, Athens suffered a serious setback, though not at the hands of Sparta. To the north of Attica the anti-democratic party in Boeotia had for some time been active. What was even more alarming was that they were receiving help and supplies from discontented elements in the island of Euboea, a fact which seemed to indicate that Euboea herself might be on the verge of revolt. This island, as I know well, was to Pericles a point of absolutely vital interest. The general principle of his strategy was, as I have already explained, that Athens was secure so long as she kept her fortifications, her ships and her empire overseas. The rest was, comparatively, of minor importance. With her sea power, Athens could draw on the resources of every land. So, though alliances with Boeotia, Phocis and other mainland states were useful, they were not essential. And in the whole empire few places were of such importance as Euboea, which not only provided Athens with much of her agricultural supplies but controlled the sea route to the north.

These were the considerations that most weighed upon Pericles when, late in the autumn, it was reported that a large band of anti-democrats from Boeotia together with exiles from Euboea and a number of ordinary adventurers from neighboring states had seized the two cities of Orchomenos and Chaeroneia in the far north of Boeotia and were planning to move southward in order to overthrow the democracy at Thebes.

At Athens the news was received in amazement and anger. There was demand for immediate action, and the general Tolmides proposed to lead out at once a volunteer force to deal with the rebels. What Myronides had done at Megara he, with better material to draw on, could, he was convinced, do easily in Boeotia. But Pericles, to the general surprise, opposed Tolmides and argued for time. The surprise was irrational, for while Pericles, as he had often enough shown, was ready enough to take risks when some vital point was at stake, he always saw further than the particular situation. His view was that an expedition such as that proposed by Tolmides should not be undertaken at all unless it was certain to be successful. Success would, admittedly, be valuable, but by failure more would be lost than could be gained by success. And while Pericles was willing to agree that success was probable, he could not affirm that it was certain. At this time of the year a large force could not be mobilized at a moment's notice; the rebel strength was unknown; and even the best tactical plans could be disrupted by elements, such as early snow or floods, which were beyond control. So he was urgent for delay and, finding for once that the people were unwilling to listen to him, said, "You may not approve of the advice of Pericles, but Time is a better counselor than anyone and you would be unwise not to recognize the fact." But the people would be guided neither by Pericles nor by Time. Tolmides received overwhelming support for his policy and within a few days set out with a force of only one thousand Athenians together with some allied contingents.

The Athenians were all volunteers and many of them were young men from the leading families, though some (Kleinias, for example) were distinguished veterans.

This was one of the very few occasions when the Assembly voted against Pericles, and it appeared at first that their decision had been correct. Tolmides advanced rapidly through Boeotia, picking up more troops on his way. He took the town of Chaeroneia and dealt with the inhabitants in the severest possible way. Not only Euripides, I remember, but many others were shocked to hear that all prisoners were to be sold as slaves. In fact this immoderate action seems to have stiffened resistance rather than undermined it. With no prospect of mercy if they surrendered, the rebels determined to fight on. Tolmides failed to take the fortress of Orchomenos and, finding difficulties in supplying his men, decided to march home. It seems that he acted with too little precaution in his march through mountainous and difficult country. His force was ambushed and surrounded near the town of Koroneia; his allies fled; half of the Athenians were killed in the fighting and the rest forced to surrender. Among the dead were Tolmides himself and also Kleinias, who left to Pericles, as his nearest kinsman, the guardianship of his two sons, one of whom, Alcibiades, was a boy of quite unusual brilliance.

In one action the Boeotian rebels had gained everything. At Athens the one desire was to recover the prisoners, and it was agreed that in exchange for them all claims to exercise control over Boeotia should be abandoned. The exiled parties came back to power in the cities. They remained distrustful of Athens and, though too weak to become open enemies, would certainly avoid any kind of understanding which might help to revive the democratic governments which they had suppressed. In the event of war, the best that Athens could hope for would be that Boeotia should remain neutral.

It was a severe blow to Athenian pride, but what chiefly alarmed Pericles was still the danger of revolt in Euboea. This danger had naturally increased because of the defeat at Koroneia. Moreover, the five-year truce with Sparta had nearly expired and so far the Spartans had been unwilling to renew it. They would now be even less likely to do so.

All the worst apprehensions were soon justified. First, the expected revolt broke out in Euboea. Pericles himself with a large force crossed over to the island. He would have taken a still larger force if it had not been necessary to leave behind a considerable army to guard the defensive positions in the Megarid in case of a Spartan invasion, for which, of course, the rebels in Euboea were hoping. Pericles's plan was, by acting with the utmost speed, to subdue Euboea before the Spartans, who are notoriously slow to move, could mobilize and bring up their forces. However, on this occasion the Spartans were unusually quick in seizing their opportunity. Pericles had scarcely begun operations in Euboea when news reached him that Megara had revolted. The Athenian garrison had been massacred and the large army under the general Andokides was cut off from Athens. The Spartans with their Peloponnesian allies had crossed the isthmus and had already reached the Athenian frontier.

Pericles made his decision at once. Abandoning Euboea, he brought his whole force back to Athens. Meanwhile Andokides, by hard marching on difficult routes, had succeeded in extricating his army and was able to join up with Pericles. The combined forces, however, were still inferior in numbers to the great army of Sparta and her allies. Athens herself could be defended and, in course of time,

the Spartans would withdraw. But it was just time that
Pericles needed. In a few more weeks the whole of Euboea
would be in arms.

In Athens itself there was bewilderment, but no panic.
It was now recognized that Pericles had been right in opposing the ill-planned adventure of Tolmides, and people
were willing to trust him absolutely in the present, far
more difficult situation. They were prepared to defend
their walls or to march out and fight. They would do
what he asked. Meanwhile the Peloponnesian army continued to advance. It reached Eleusis, one day's march
from Athens, and began to move down the Sacred Way
towards the last ridge of hills before the city — the place
from which Xerxes, on his golden throne, had watched
the battle of Salamis. It is, of course, a Spartan custom
that the army should be under the command of one of the
two kings, and on this occasion the king who held the post
was Pleistoanax, a very young man, in fact guided entirely
by a senior and distinguished Spartan officer, Kleandridas,
who had already shown on this campaign exceptional skill
and energy. Pericles knew something of the man himself
and much of the Spartan character in general. He had perfectly clear ideas of what were the essential interests of
Athens and was prepared, if necessary, to sacrifice much
in order to secure them. Now, above all, he needed time in
order to reduce Euboea. He knew too that Spartans, in
spite of, or possibly because of, the extreme rigidity of their
moral code, are peculiarly vulnerable to bribery. He therefore made secret contact with Kleandridas and explained
to him that Athens was now prepared to make large concessions for the sake of peace, but that if it was to be war she
was perfectly ready for it and had the power to land men
at any spot she chose on the Peloponnesian coast. And, to
make matters easier, he offered a large sum of money to be

paid to Kleandridas in person as soon as he had withdrawn his army beyond the isthmus. No one except Pericles himself and a few others knew of these negotiations. There was therefore as much surprise as relief when scouts rode in to report that the great enemy force had broken camp and was retiring by the way it had come.

In Sparta itself there was not only surprise but anger. The young king was put on trial and exiled. Kleandridas preferred not to await trial. He fled abroad and was condemned to death in absence. He had a distinguished career later as a general in Italy, and seems to have been one of the few Spartans who has not been wholly corrupted by having money to spend.

In Athens people were mystified by what had happened, until Pericles, in putting forward his accounts to the appropriate committee at the end of the year, included an expenditure of ten talents, paid, he said, for "necessary reasons." As Pericles's scrupulous care in accounting was well known, nobody had much doubt about how this sum had been spent and everyone was amused by his method of revealing the fact.

As soon as the Spartans had withdrawn Pericles set out again for Euboea with fifty ships and five thousand men. It was a short and brilliant campaign. In a matter of months the whole island was reduced. One town, the inhabitants of which had captured an Athenian ship and massacred the whole crew, was treated with severity, the whole population being expelled from their territory. Otherwise there were no reprisals, though the precaution was taken of settling another large Athenian colony in the north of the island. In the winter Pericles, with Kallias and Andokides, went to Sparta to negotiate peace. Pericles was prepared to make great concessions as he had promised, but not to concede anything that seemed to him vital; after his victories in Euboea he was in a good position to resist such inevitable Spartan demands as the withdrawal of Athens from Aegina and from the Gulf of Corinth. His eyes had always been on the sea and to him the essential positions were Aegina and the town of Naupactus on the Gulf, garrisoned by those Messenians whose loyalty could be absolutely depended upon. He agreed, however, to withdraw from the Peloponnese and from Megara with its two harbors. On this basis was signed the treaty for a thirty-year peace, a peace which did, in fact, last for fifteen years. It was the first time since Salamis that Athens had not been engaged in either one or two major wars.

11

◻◻◻◻◻

Activity in Leisure

IN THE FOLLOWING YEAR I saw more of Pericles and his
household than I had seen for some time. This was because Pericles himself had more leisure than usual, for it was
one of the few years in which he was not elected to the
board of generals. He correctly estimated that after the
terms of the peace were known his popularity would decline and that it would soon be recovered. For the Athenians are not always rational. Most of them were glad to
have peace and many of them were aware that in making
it Pericles had gained much and lost little. Yet still they
found it almost intolerable to withdraw from any position
which they had once occupied. So, for a very short time,
Pericles was out of favor, though before the end of the year
the people were listening to him with all their old eager-
ness and attention whenever he spoke in the Assembly.

In his private life he had some disappointments and,
apart from his friends, one great consolation and delight.
He could feel no pride in his two sons, Paralos and Xanthippus, both of whom were extravagant and one of whom was
rude, bad-tempered and uncouth. Obviously neither of

them was fitted for any position of distinction. They were resentful of their father for his economic habits and indeed expected nothing from him except money. They were quite incapable of following his thought or understanding his character. His two wards, the sons of Kleinias, who had died with Tolmides at Koroneia, were no more satisfactory. One of these boys, called after his father, was almost half-witted. The other, Alcibiades, had all the charm, brilliance and energy of the Alcmaeonidae. He was good-looking, strong, ambitious and remarkably intelligent. He was also ruthless, extravagant, self-willed and vicious. His aim was always for distinction — a good aim, if pursued with virtue and humanity. But Alcibiades would be, by any means, the first in everything. They say that once, when wrestling with a stronger boy, he was in danger of being thrown and, to avoid defeat, fastened his teeth into the other boy's arm. The boy was shocked and astonished. "Alcibiades," he said, "you bite like a girl."

"No," said Alcibiades. "Like a lion."

In my view, if Alcibiades had been able to feel sympathy for his guardian, he might, with all his fine qualities (for he was not only physically but intellectually admirable), have become a man of whom Pericles himself might be proud. His patriotism is as great as that of Pericles; his intellectual powers not much inferior. Yet while Pericles was absorbed in Athens, Alcibiades, I think, would absorb Athens in himself. He is like one of those lovers who, rather than lose the object of their affections, would destroy it. Such lovers describe themselves as devoted, but they are devoted more to their own passions than to the thing which excites them.

Very different was the love which Pericles felt both for Athens and for individual men and women. And his love for one woman would be remarkable in any man. Almost equally remarkable is the fact that Aspasia not only returned but deserved his affection. It was about this time that she first came to live with him, and she remained his companion for the rest of his life. She is, of course, an Ionian from Miletus and she had not been long in Athens before she attracted the attention of Pericles. She was then a young woman about twenty years old and belonged to that class which is called in Athens the "Hetairai." These women are very different from common prostitutes, though they too make their living by the pleasures of their company. But in their case the pleasures which they confer are not entirely or even mainly physical. Most of them are intelligent, used to the company of men and at ease in conversation. For these reasons the ordinary Athenian housewife expresses contempt for them, but feels envy. Aspasia in particular aroused their anger because she had none of the faults which they attribute indiscriminately to her class. She remained faithful to one man (which is more than can be said of most housewives) and, since Pericles was known for his moderate style of living, she could scarcely be accused of seeking him out for the sake of money. It was easier to make jokes at the expense of Pericles himself and to say that he, who was now fifty years old, was weakly yielding to an infatuation unsuited to his age and experience, behaving like the great Heracles when enslaved by Omphale, or like Zeus himself who, under the spell of Hera's attractions, was lulled to sleep when he should have been active. Some even suggested that if he could show such extraordinary devotion to one woman he must necessarily feel the same devotion to a great many more and be a secret libertine, constantly in pursuit of other men's wives. Such gossip was, as a rule, harmless. The Athenians enjoy nothing so much as finding what they imagine to be a weak point in one of their leaders whom they most admire. But, as I know from my own experience, there are times in Athens when people become wholly swayed by prejudice, and at such times they will believe any scandal, however stupid and however demonstrably untrue. I myself and many others, including Aspasia, have suffered from these outbreaks of malice and unreason.

It seems to me that in his conduct toward Aspasia, Pericles was setting a standard which, like all his standards, was unusually high and which is deserving of imitation. He was in the habit of giving her a kiss when he left the house and when he returned to it. People regarded this as most peculiar, but to my mind there is nothing at all peculiar in demonstrations of affection that are both graceful and sincere. It is undoubtedly rare for a man not to soon grow tired of a woman, but it is impossible to maintain that everything rare is undesirable. I believe that Pericles and Aspasia enjoyed more satisfaction from each others' company and conferred more genuine benefits, each on each, than any other pair of human beings belonging to opposite sexes with whom I have been acquainted. And I think that if such a state of mutual enjoyment and understanding were more common, it would be an advantage not only to the parents but to the children. Certainly the child who was born later to Pericles and Aspasia was in every way a much finer character than either Xanthippus or Paralos.

We Ionians like to think (and we have reason for it) that our women are remarkable for their grace of manner and of person, their strong affections and their pleasant vivacity. Aspasia possessed all these qualities to the full and also had intellectual qualities which would be exceptional in either sex or in any country. She had a naturally quick intelligence and much knowledge; nor was she satisfied, as many people far less informed than she was often are, with the knowledge that she possessed. She would discuss philosophy with me as readily as poetry with Sophocles or politics with Pericles, and her conversation on these subjects was at least as stimulating to us as in all probability ours was to her. No wonder that we took pleasure in her company!

A regular guest of Pericles at this time was the sculptor Pheidias, a man who, apart altogether from his extraordinary genius in the working of bronze, marble, gold and ivory, was gifted with an original and farseeing mind. He was older than Pericles and indeed not much younger than I, but was only just beginning to come into his fame. He was known then chiefly for the great bronze statue of Athene the Champion which had recently been completed. All of you who have visited Athens will have seen this statue, famous not only for its size (it is at least thirty feet in height) but for the splendor of its conception. His later statues in gold and ivory of Athene in the Parthenon and of Zeus at Olympia are, of course, known and admired throughout the world. They are rightly regarded as the finest representations of divinity that have ever been produced by man. Some people regard this as odd, because Pheidias, like myself, was prosecuted for impiety, and it is only in a rather special sense that either of us can be said to believe in the gods. For the gods are not objects of natural inquiry. I have yet to meet a man who has seen a god, except in dreams, and it seems obvious that Xenophanes is right in saying that the qualities which we attribute to the gods cannot be other than those which we know ourselves. If horses had gods, these gods would partake of the nature of a horse. It is therefore evidently mistaken to suppose that the gods have faces and limbs like ours, are either male or female, or that they speak Greek. Many people, on the basis of such consideration, have concluded either that no gods exist or that, if they do, they must be totally incomprehensible to us, but neither of these conclusions seems to me legitimate. Apart from man there are other existences in nature which we recognize and, in varying degrees, understand. No man, or anything like a man, controls the movements of the moon and stars or the process by which one state of being is transformed into another. The events of human life too do not wholly conform to a pattern of reason and of justice. Most men are disquieted when they observe such facts, and the more simple-minded attribute what is incomprehensible to the actions, beneficent, malevolent or capricious, of various deities. This merely adds one problem to another, for if we are to believe in gods at all, we must believe them to be wiser and better than men. I, as you know, have put forward the theory of a creative force, which I call intelligence, and which I assume to bring order out of disorder, justice out of injustice and to be the principle, in various modifications, of change and of motion. That such a thing exists we cannot, in the nature of things, be certain, but a good man, unless he can find some better explanation for things, will not be mistaken in believing that there is some truth in what I say.

Pericles, Pheidias, Damon and Euripides (among others) have all been deeply interested in my views and all of them have been accused by the ignorant of atheism. In fact we are looking for principles more exalted and consistent than are to be found in the self-contradictions and crudities of mythology and the effect of our speculations will be to purify, not to debase, popular religion. For one can imagine no kind of god capable of approving a man who believes in what is demonstrably untrue.

Yet even error can, by the force of intelligence, be shaped in the direction of truth, and Pheidias as much as any man has succeeded in doing this. He knows as well as I do that gods do not have arms and legs, hair and eyes; but it is also true that there do genuinely exist in nature qualities which we rightly think of as higher than others — beauty, for instance, intelligence, goodness and serenity. To depict a god in any kind of shape — human, animal, vegetable or mineral — is, of course, inaccurate; but so long as the shape is endowed with such qualities as those I have mentioned, it will provoke a kind of reverence and the result will be, from a human point of view, both delightful and useful, and, from a philosophical point of view, not necessarily misleading. If one wishes merely to illustrate the variety and contradiction of the universe, with its alternations of good and evil, beauty and disfigurement, being and not-being, it may be more appropriate to do as the Egyptians do and produce images of men with the heads of crocodiles, dogs and cats. And from the old temples of the Acropolis which were destroyed by the Persians there still survive fragments of sculptured monsters which are not without significance. Those works which emphasize the forces of vision, creation and stability are more significant, however, and more useful than those which merely signify the strength and terror of what is uncontrolled and, because disorderly, savage. This, at least, is the view of an Ionian and a Greek, and, as is shown by the tremendous reputation of Pheidias, it is a view that is very generally held.

Such considerations as these frequently formed the theme of our conversations at this time, for it was now, in the years of peace, that were begun and so rapidly completed those great schemes of building, sculpture, decoration and amenity which have made Athens incomparably the finest city in the world. Pheidias was the general supervisor of all these works and he owed this splendid opportunity to his friendship with Pericles, who would discuss with him every detail, help him in all branches of administration, and supply and defend vigorously in the Assembly the whole ambitious plan against his political opponents who complained of waste of money and unjustifiable diversion of the tribute of the allies to the glorification of Athens.

It was natural, therefore, that in these days we talked much of the problems of architecture, sculpture and painting. These problems are interesting in themselves, but what was surprising and exciting was to see them being solved so rapidly and so perfectly. I myself found these conversations most interesting from a philosophical point of view; for it has always seemed to me that the principles of art are the same as the principles of nature. What we see depends on what is unseen, and a state of perfection is a state of balanced contradiction, of a synthesis of opposites, of tension resolved in peace. In the Parthenon, for instance, the tremendous weight of the structure, which is evident if one examines it with one's vision limited to one section or estimates the sheer quantity of marble that has been used, has, when seen as a whole, a quality of supernatural lightness. The lines seem to soar into the sky and then to cease at an upper limit; yet in the whole building there is not one straight line, and one can hardly say there is a limit, since this work of art is made miraculously in adjustment with its natural surroundings, the sea, the sky, the mountains and the plain. But here again I digress. All of you who have been to Athens will know and will have wondered at these productions. They are works made possible by the most precise exercise of mathematics, by the keenest and most humane intelligence. Pheidias was the master artist, Callicrates, Ictinus and Mnesicles were architects of the most extraordinary brilliance, subtlety, insight and imagination. The inspiration was that of Pericles, and the force and impetus was from the directed energy and enthusiasm of the Athenian people. If anything on earth can be im-

mortal, these constructions of flesh, blood and intellect
will remain so.

These works were done once and were done forever. A
due consideration of them may lead one into speculation
upon the nature of time and of motion, and I hope, before
I die, to set down something of what I have been able to
think or imagine on these enormously important subjects.
The memory of that time still fills me with wonder, even
though I was then occupied in very different and, it now
seems to me, subordinate pursuits. Not that the researches
which I was making into the rarefaction and condensation
of air are insignificant. Obviously they are of very great importance indeed. The difference between a Greek and a
barbarian is, apart from the language, in the fact that a
Greek wants to know and to explain. And for knowledge
both observation and experiment are necessary. Yet in
knowledge and beyond knowledge, in the final act of explanation, the mind must, as it were, leap into darkness and
find there a bright place to rest. Pheidias in his great works
and Sophocles too and Pericles seem to have done something like this. Out of the ferment, energy and contradiction of life they have constructed intellectual shapes of
beauty, satisfaction and truth.

I myself at this time had already been working for some
years in collaboration with my friend the Athenian Archelaus, whom you know. Others apart from our old circle
would often come to take part in our philosophical discussions and investigations. Among the young men who used
to visit us regularly I remember one in particular, since he,
almost in the same way as the artists whom I have mentioned, seems to combine very great strength of intellect
with a singular freshness and adventurousness of spirit.
His name is Socrates and I should not be surprised if in the
end he becomes better known than he is now. When I

first met him I thought him the ugliest young man I had
ever seen. He looks not only as strong as a bear but rather
like one. But one has only to be with him for a few min-
utes to become amazed and delighted by his wit, his charm,
his ready consideration for others and his extraordinarily
keen intelligence. He had taken part in the recent campaign of Andokides in the Megarid when great dangers had
been escaped by almost incredible exertions on the part of
the army. Even in this army he had impressed his fellow
soldiers with his apparently total indifference to heat, cold,
danger or fatigue. It was not that, it seems, like many
young soldiers, he was trying to gain a reputation for courage and endurance; it was simply, they said, that it never
occurred to him to think of cowardice or weariness. Socrates
used to reply that if this was true, he deserved no credit at
all; it was impossible to know one quality or experience one
sensation without also knowing the opposite one; a man
who knows nothing of cowardice can know nothing of
courage either; if, therefore, his conduct had really been
what it was described, he should be treated with commis-
eration rather than with honor, for no one can be called
virtuous who is so stupid and insensitive as not to be able
to tell good from evil.

But I am digressing, led astray by the many and happy
memories of that time. Now Pericles is dead; Pheidias,
Damon and I are in exile; Socrates has, for all I know, died
in battle or of the plague. Yet whether in death or exile the
fact stands that we lived in Athens at that time and were
uniquely happy in doing so. Now Sophocles and Euripides
still produce their plays, and when I read them I consider
that they write with greater skill and wisdom than ever; yet
still I find lacking some element that was always present in
those days. I am reminded of a phrase that Pericles once
used in one of the official speeches made in honor of those

who had died in battle. "The spring," he said, "has gone out of the year." The fleets of Athens still control the sea; the people still react to disaster with resolution and to opportunity with ambition. Yet now I seem to detect a kind of feverishness in their enterprise, a lack of ease in their confidence. Athens too, no doubt, insofar as it is an organization of men, is subject to the general laws of growth and decay. Yet there is a sense in which it may be said that she has already transcended those laws. Like other states, she has been guilty of crime and injustice. Unlike any other state, she has aimed at an excellence that may prove to be beyond the powers of human nature, and, however the process ends, her success has been more than partial. To those of us who know her, her faults seem, if regrettable, incidental. What we love in her is something which, through being faultless, must prove eternal.

12

□ □ □ □ □

The Last Opposition

WITHIN A YEAR, as I have said, Pericles was re-elected
to the board of generals and continued to be elected
year after year for the rest of his life. At first he had to face
some opposition. This came principally from the remains of
the old party of Kimon, who were now led by a younger relation of his, Thucydides the son of Melesias. This opposition,
though it enjoyed some successes, failed to have any real
effect on the policies of Pericles, which continued to be carried out logically and consistently to the end and received a
more and more overwhelming popular support. It is significant that another and much younger relative of Kimon's,
also called Thucydides, became one of the most fervent admirers of Pericles whom I have ever met. He is a young man
of quite remarkable intelligence and will very probably, I
think, make a name for himself. Recently he has been kind
enough to send me from Athens some notes which he set
down of some of the last speeches which Pericles ever made.
He has caught the style well, and, more important still, has
seen, underlying the style, the fervent passion of the man, a
passion to which young Thucydides evidently responds.

I think that his elderly relative, Thucydides the son of Melesias, was an honest and generous man, and his antagonism to Pericles was, like that of Kimon, political rather than personal. He fought, as it were in the last ditch, for that old and discredited policy of friendship with Sparta and, in home politics, a return to the old, simple aristocratic ways which existed before Athens came to depend for her life and her enterprise on the sea. He was, in a way, more reactionary than Kimon, looking back to a past that seemed to him stationary only because he had never known it. Kimon had lived with the fleet, and though he resented what seemed to him the extravagant political demands of those who served with him, he still respected them as men and as comrades. Moreover, he had become, perhaps somewhat thoughtlessly, committed to the course of empire. Ideally, he would have liberated all Greeks except those in subjection to Sparta.

Thucydides was more logical, if less human. He considered that the old prestige and authority of the ancient families and of the landed aristocracy in general were gradually being submerged by people of new and different ideas and ways of life, people whose interests were on the sea, in trade, in empire and in politics rather than in their farms —"a rabble of sailors and dockworkers," he used to call them in private conversation. He saw Piraeus as the enemy of Athens and regarded the great new buildings and admirably designed thoroughfares and markets and depots and dockyards, which were now, under the direction of Pericles, making Piraeus the greatest and best organized seaport of the world, as a menace and a challenge to the city itself. It was, in his view, because of the support of this "rabble of sailors" that Ephialtes and Pericles had been able to strip the Areopagus Council of its old powers and bring in a system by which nearly everyone in the state was eligible not only for office and responsibility but for payment or subsidy. The true tradition of Athens, he claimed, was that of Miltiades, Xanthippus, Aristides and Kimon, not that of Themistocles and Pericles.

It must be owned that he accepted many of the logical consequences, however unpopular, of these views. He saw as well as Pericles himself that the structure of the democracy as it now was depended for its expansion, and even for its maintenance, on the resources of the empire, and that to preserve the empire it was necessary for Athens to have naval superiority in all seas. Therefore, since his chief aim was to prevent the expansion of the democracy, he was prepared to abandon the empire. Friendship with Sparta seemed to him worth this price, and of course he was able to make use of some arguments which appeared to have moral force. He was, for instance, never tired of accusing Pericles of dishonesty in diverting the money paid by the allies toward a fund for defense into schemes for the beautification of Athens. But these arguments were seldom effective, partly because the great public works gave employment and interest to so many, partly because Pericles did in fact represent the enterprise and ambition of the time. Both Pericles and Thucydides were skilled debaters, but Pericles had one asset which his opponent lacked. As I have often said, he always, and in a most remarkable way, appealed to reason, but in doing so his manner was as impressive as his argument, with such calm and conviction did he speak. It seemed impossible to believe that he could be wrong. Hence, I suppose, his nickname of "the Olympian." It was not that he regarded himself as superior to other men; it was rather that he could not help appearing to be so. Thucydides used to say, "He is like a wrestler whom it is impossible to beat. When I give him a fall in argument, he gets to his feet, claims that he was never thrown, and actually convinces the spectators that he is speaking the truth."

Probably the most effective political tactic that Thucydides devised was to group the members of his party into a body which always sat together at meetings of the Assembly, applauded together and in general gave a greater impression of unanimity and enthusiasm than was, perhaps, justified. Among the rest of the Assembly there were some, particularly among the small farmers, who, seeing so many of the rich and the distinguished — people whom they had been brought up to respect — all gathered in one group and all apparently united, came to the conclusion that there must be some sense in what they were saying. And Thucydides was a clever enough politician not to say what he really meant. He knew that it would be impossible to find a majority in the Assembly willing to alter the constitution in any evidently reactionary way, or to make any further concessions to Sparta that could possibly be avoided. Indeed, the only reason why, for a short time, people were dissatisfied with Pericles was that he had made any concessions at all. Yet, except in times of quite extraordinary and unprecedented success, people are always apt to contrast the present unfavorably with the past. They soon forget what was bad in the past and it takes time to realize what is good in the present. The Athenians, in particular, scarcely seem to live in the present at all. They live either in the past or in the future. This is a fact which Pericles knew well, and he more than any statesman combined the deepest reverence for the past with an enlightened and dynamic leadership into the future.

Thucydides was, of necessity, somewhat confined to the past, but in Athens it is always possible for anyone with sufficient skill to impress an audience with reflections about "the good old days," in which it is assumed, particularly by the older men, that people were happier and more virtuous

than they are now. One method of discrediting Pericles was
to suggest that he was, from a moral or religious point of
view, unorthodox and must therefore be unreliable politically. But it was difficult to make such attacks at all convincing if they were made against Pericles himself. Everyone
knew well that he was, unlike many of his opponents, ab-
stemious, courteous, honest and patriotic. His great and
devoted attachment to Aspasia had surprised most people
and shocked some, but no one took seriously, though many
found amusement in, stories to the effect that he was a
seducer of noble women and that Pheidias, under cover of
showing these ladies round the new works of sculpture and
architecture, was in fact employed by Pericles as a procurer.
It was even said that specimens of that very rare and beautiful bird the peacock, which had recently been brought to
Athens for the first time, had been specially imported by
Pericles to serve as gifts or bribes for his mistresses.

In cases (and there were not many of them) where the
principal opponent was unassailable, it was normal to seek
to discredit him by making attacks on his friends. A good
man will, as a rule, have good friends; but one can always
attack the good so long as it is either unknown or capable
of misrepresentation. Many of the friends of Pericles were
known to and admired by all — Sophocles, for example.
But there were others, including myself, who were known
chiefly by reputation and, partly for that reason, were objects of suspicion. It could be said truly that we were unorthodox in some of our views and it could be assumed unjustly
that these views were subversive of society. I myself was
alarmed when a half-crazed monger of oracles called Dio-
peithes managed to excite the Assembly into passing a decree in condemnation of those who do not believe in the
gods and who teach things about the heavenly bodies. I
realized that if I were to be summoned before the courts on

a charge of impiety, I should find it hard to explain to a prejudiced jury the arguments which have led me to assert that the sun is made of molten rock and is much larger than it appears to be, and that my views about the gods would only be intelligible to men who have themselves thought deeply on the subject.

However, on this occasion I was spared, partly because Pericles very soon regained his position of ascendancy, partly because his enemies were in pursuit of others more politically important than myself. During the years immediately following the peace there were several attempts to get rid of citizens, by means of ostracism, who were known to be associated with the policies of Pericles; but if Thucydides and his advisers hoped to get rid of Pericles himself in this way, they were shown to be mistaken, and it was not long before their own methods were employed against them. Scarcely a single vote was cast against Pericles himself. His friends, however, were not equally fortunate, and one of the oldest of these, Damon, was, by one of these votes, forced to go into exile. This was a bitter blow to Pericles and to many of us. It was also a misuse of the method of ostracism, which in my view is a valuable political expedient only when there are two sharply contrasting policies in the state, one of which, from necessity, has to be adopted; and in such cases it is obviously desirable that the man who should be required to go into exile should be one or the other of the leaders of the two parties. But Thucydides had no positive policy, or rather, he did not venture to disclose it; and Damon, though an intimate friend of Pericles, had taken very little part in active politics. Thus the vote against Damon served no useful political purpose. Most of those who inscribed his name on the fragments of pottery which were used for the voting were actuated by no worthier feelings than mischief and malice. Later many of them became ashamed of these feelings and, to salve their consciences, turned against Thucydides the resentment that they really felt against themselves.

The final defeat of Thucydides followed upon and was partly associated with the important new foundation of Sybaris in southern Italy. This was a project which Pericles himself had supported and for the organization of which he was largely responsible. It deserves, I think, more than a passing mention, since to him it represented not only an extension of Athenian influence into the west, but also an example of how Athens could cooperate with other states in a venture that was Hellenic rather than national. He intended, of course, that here, as in other respects, the attitude of Athens should be contrasted with that of Sparta, for when, a few years before, a deputation had come from Italy to ask both Sparta and Athens for help in making the new foundation, Sparta had declined to have anything to do with it. The deputation was from the descendants of the ancient city of Sybaris, which in its time had become proverbial for its wealth and luxury. Now nearly sixty years had passed since this great city had been destroyed by the forces of the Pythagorean brotherhood who were in control of the neighboring city of Kroton. Here, if I may digress, I should like to state my view that these Pythagoreans, who formed themselves into a political organization with the avowed intention of forcing other men to adopt their strange notions of purity and righteousness, were acting in a manner most unsuitable to philosophers. And I fear that some responsibility must attach to Pythagoras himself, who, while he lived in Samos, appears to have been a sensible man, but after settling in Italy is credited with believing that he was divine. Something of the same sort often happens to Ionians and other Greeks who go west. Empedocles of Sicily, for instance, fancies that he is a god, and Parmenides gives the impression that he holds the same belief about himself. Not that I would belittle the real merits and important discoveries of Pythagoras in mathematics and in the theory of music. But the very success of these discoveries seems to have induced him into extravagance. He believed the whole universe to be mathematical and musical; he neglected observation and made numbers into gods.

Now we Ionians, from the time of Thales onwards, have attempted to explain the universe by means of some general principle; we have, of course, observed that appearance is not the same as reality; but we have never taken the absurd step of denying that appearance exists. As I have expressed it myself, "What appears is a vision of the unseen." But Pythagoras seems to believe that only the unseen exists. Such a way of thought must end in inhumanity. He states that "the body is a tomb," implying that only the soul has a real and valid existence. This phrase appears to me meaningless, and of course it must lead to all kinds of philosophical contradictions. But here I am rather concerned with the dangerous political and moral implications of this thinking. For if one denies the body, one must turn one's back not only on the evidence of our senses but on all human life as it is normally lived. And indeed the followers of Pythagoras will declare that nothing is of importance except the purification of the soul. This is a very different doctrine from our normal assumption that a man should aim at excellence, for in our idea of excellence we include beauty, intelligence, strength, justice and many other qualities, social, physical and intellectual. But the Pythagorean, concerned uniquely with the purification of his own soul, will not, if he is consistent, enter the field of action in which virtues grow and are exemplified. He regards such action as a kind of pollution of his own true nature, which is mathematical or musical or both and, in his own view, divine.

One would imagine, therefore, that a Pythagorean would take no part in human affairs, or the smallest part possible, since all action that is not musical or mathematical is impure. And this, it seems, was originally the doctrine. A way of life was devised to cut off the believer from ordinary human society. There were strict rules of austerity and a number of peculiar prohibitions concerning meat, beans, bed linen and white cocks.

Yet human nature, when repressed, is apt to assert itself. It is natural for a human being to enter into political and social relationships with others; indeed, it is not only natural but good, and in a democracy such as that in which I have lived at Athens, personal relations are as free and easy as possible. I know that even in Athens inconsistencies are to be found. Damon suffered at this time, I suffered later, and no doubt others will also suffer from a sudden storm of stupidity and intolerance. But in general the Athenians pride themselves chiefly on their freedom and take more precautions to safeguard it than any other people. They do this both instinctively and with reason. They would listen to Pericles as to a friend and an oracle as he explained to them that happiness was impossible without freedom, since only in freedom could a man so develop and strengthen all his manifold capacities as to be a delight and a benefit to himself and others. This it is, finally, that distinguishes the Athenians from the Spartans and indeed from all people. And it is impossible for a person lacking in modesty to understand or to implement this notion of freedom. Pericles, in spite of his superior gifts, would only impose his will on the Athenians by means of persuasion, because he believed each one of them to be important both individually and for the general good. And I have been led to write so much of these Pythagoreans in Italy not because they deserve much attention in themselves, but because they seem apt to illustrate a way of thought wholly different from and greatly inferior to that of Pericles.

To begin with, they were inconsistent, and Pericles was never inconsistent. Instead of retiring from the world and, in some seclusion, cultivating their "souls," which they desired to see separated from their bodies, they took it upon themselves to reform the world without any consideration for any views and desires other than their own. In the Italian cities they formed themselves into narrow aristocracies of piety which dominated the great mass of the citizens in the various states that came under their control. They justified conduct that would normally be called injustice by the theory that it is important to do good to people even against their wills. Pericles, of course, did not believe such a thing to be possible. One cannot be good without freedom. Thus he could use words in the normal sense. On the occasions when he employed coercion, he never pretended that coercion was good, only that it was necessary. He was choosing, he considered, a lesser evil, but was aware that it was an evil. The Pythagoreans did evil in the mistaken belief that it was good. So before long they were involved in all the crimes and exaggerations of tyranny, which as it became more hypocritical became more violent. One of their actions was, as I have said, the destruction of the great city of Sybaris, which, pleasure-loving and democratic, seemed to threaten not only their material interests but their way of life. This act of barbarism was one of the last of their achievements. Before long there were revolutions, as might have been expected, in all the states under their control. Many of them were killed, many driven into exile. The survivors did what they should have done in the first place, if they had been logical, and devoted all their attention to philosophy. Since then they have done useful work in mathematics. But I should not be surprised if, at some future date, they should attempt to regain political and autocratic power. This always happens with groups of men who are intolerant of diversity.

Pericles, who in Athens had most to do with welcoming the deputation of the Sybarites and with the foundation of the new city in Italy, showed a wholly different spirit and indeed greatly surprised his political opponents. He had been accused by them of pressing the interests of Athens too far forward at the expense of others, particularly of the allies. Quite recently he had spoken in favor of making alliances with the Sicilian cities of Leontini and Egesta, and Thucydides had claimed that this was another step in the direction of dangerously extending Athenian commitments in the west. But now, with regard to this new settlement, he showed his willingness to conciliate enemies and to exert the influence of Athens by generosity rather than compulsion. The two leaders of the colonists were Athenians, but colonists from all parts of Greece, including the Dorian states of the Peloponnese, were invited to join the expedition. Thucydides himself was to accompany it and to remain until the settlement was firmly established. The Athenians were to have no exclusive rights in the new venture, only the prestige of leadership and planning. There is, of course, no doubt that Pericles hoped that in the end the Athenian methods of government and administration would be accepted voluntarily by the rest and that the new settlement would become an ally of Athens; but what is significant is that he did not attempt to secure this result by any kind of compulsion, nor, when his hopes were disappointed, did he attempt to alter the progress of events. This I consider to be public evidence of what I and many others know privately — that where the vital present interests of Athenian security were concerned Pericles was inflexible, but that when he thought of the future he thought in terms

of a generous cooperation among Greeks. Certainly he believed that under such conditions the Athenians would become accepted as leaders, but he wished that this leadership should be, like his own in Athens, based rather on
skill and persuasion than on the assertion of armed force.

I myself am well informed about this colony, since many
of my friends were among the colonists. Some were very
distinguished men. There was, for instance, Hippodamos
of Miletus, the town planner, who in consultation with
Pericles had been responsible for all the new building in
Piraeus. He was one of the first to recognize the obvious
advantages, from the point of view of traffic control, of
broad straight thoroughfares intersecting each other at
right angles. As a result of his work you can travel in
Piraeus twice the distance that you could cover in the same
time in Athens. Then there was another Ionian, Herodotus
of Halicarnassus, one of the wittiest and most learned men
I have ever met and a great traveler. He was already a
friend of Pericles, and Sophocles had written a poem in
his honor; and this was before the time when his great history was completed. Pericles had been much impressed by
those portions of the history which he had seen and later
was responsible for awarding to Herodotus the greatest
literary prize in terms of money that has ever been given to
a Greek. And this was not because Herodotus was his
friend or even because in his history he rightly emphasizes
the great part played by Athens in the Persian wars. It was
because his work was excellent, original and, insofar as this
is possible in history, true. Pericles believed that it was the
duty and privilege of Athens to support and encourage everything that is excellent.

Another of the colonists was Protagoras of Abdera, also
a man of very great learning, though I should hardly call
him a philosopher. He, like most of the others who are

called "sophists," was more interested in acquiring and using knowledge for practical political purposes than in investigating the fundamental nature of the universe. Indeed, many of these sophists will declare that the discovery of truth is impossible or that, if it were possible, the knowledge of it could never be communicated to others. You will still find many people who quote the statement of Protagoras that "man is the measure" as a justification for their own selfishness, lethargy, lack of curiosity and ignorance. In fact this statement, about which we hear so much, can only be interpreted as meaning something that is perfectly obvious or something that is obviously untrue. But Protagoras is a good man whose views on all practical matters are well worth attention. He was given the responsibility for drawing up the constitution of the new colony, and I am told that he did this work admirably, though to the distaste of the original Sybarites, who expected, for no good reason, to occupy a position of particular privilege.

In fact there were, as often happens, many difficulties and disagreements before the city finally took shape at Thouria, near the site of ancient Sybaris. Thucydides himself was involved in one of these quarrels, and when he returned to Athens he was prosecuted by one of the two Athenian founders. There was also trouble with some of the neighboring Italian cities, and the people of Thouria were lucky in being able to secure the services of the exiled Spartan Kleandridas, who was a fine soldier, though, as Pericles had discovered, easy to bribe. Today Thouria is a rich and prosperous city. Herodotus, after another stay in Athens, has returned to live there and is honored as one of its leading citizens. It is one of those places which bears the mark of Athens without being an Athenian dependency, and this is what Pericles wanted it to be.

It so happened (and this was, of course, pure accident)

that the venture of Thouria turned out very much to Pericles's own political advantage. Thucydides, after his prosecution for events connected with the expedition, became, rightly or wrongly, extremely unpopular. In the recent past he had attempted to discredit Pericles by attacking his friends and, most unsuccessfully, to get rid of Pericles himself by means of ostracism. He now suffered what he had planned for others. A vote by ostracism was held and Thucydides was forced to go into exile for ten years. For the rest of Pericles's life there was no resolute or important opposition to his leadership.

13

□□□□□

The War with Samos

A STRIKING EXAMPLE of the complete ascendancy which Pericles had now won over the Athenian people can be found in the war with Samos, which broke out soon after the ostracism of Thucydides. In this war the Athenians lost many lives and were, for a short time, in great danger. The war was violently opposed by the remnants of Thucydides's party, who asserted that Athens was acting with a complete disregard for justice and her own safety. They were supported by several of the comic poets, who did their best to deride Pericles by harping on his supposed meanness and his infatuation for Aspasia. The people laughed at the jokes, but continued to support Pericles enthusiastically in everything that he suggested to them.

At the time when this war broke out Samos was by far the most powerful of the allies. Her long naval tradition went back to the times of the tyrant Polycrates, who is said to have designed the first modern warships and who made the city of Samos, before the Persian conquest, into one of the richest and most brilliant in the world. The Samians claim with some reason that in those days they were preeminent not only in shipbuilding but in architecture, engineering and poetry. Among their philosophers they could name Pythagoras, about whom I have already declared my opinion. Samos still possessed a powerful fleet and, with the other large islands of Chios and Lesbos, still provided ships rather than money as her contribution to the Athenian alliance. As a result she was used to considering herself independent. The Athenians had made no attempt to shape or control her government as they had done in the case of the great mainland city of Miletus.

It was because of a dispute with Miletus, which had long been a rival of Samos and could boast of an equally distinguished past (much more distinguished, so far as philosophy is concerned), that the war broke out, although, in my opinion, the occasions for war can seldom be regarded as their true causes. In Samos there was a strong anti-democratic party which felt itself threatened by the increasing prestige of the democracies, which of course were, as a rule, supported by Athens. But nationalism can be at least as powerful a force as democracy, and it seemed possible to bring even their political opponents into a common effort to secure complete independence which, if won, would secure the anti-democrats in power. In such a situation war was, in any case, likely if not inevitable. The same thing may be said of the present war, the outbreak of which did not depend on any particular dispute, but simply on the fact that the Spartans realized that as Athens grew stronger, their own position must inevitably grow weaker.

So, with regard to this war with Samos, the events which immediately led up to it are of only incidental importance. Nor would it be wholly accurate to say that the real cause of the war was in the conflicting interests of democracy and a system by which power went, as a matter of course, to the rich and noble families. This explanation is indeed nearer the truth, but the issue was confused by the fact that the Athenian democracy, the model for all democracies, was also, and of necessity, an imperialism. It was possible, and almost reasonable, for a Samian democrat to regard any Athenian intervention in his affairs as an attack upon his liberty. Pericles, of course, was aware of this attitude and could sympathize with it. But his greatness lies in the fact that he was a realist as well as a theoretician. What is vital must be defended at all costs, and in his view Athens herself, the leader and example of all liberty and of every brilliant hope, depended for her existence and survival on the maintenance of her empire. Freedom, to him, was more than a word or a sensation of irresponsibility. He imagined it rather as the outcome of security, initiative and an integration of both delicacy and strength. He could be ruthless, but he could not be inhuman, sentimental or hypocritical. Unlike other statesmen, he realized the full implications of any decision that he made, but he was not for that reason any the less quick in coming to a decision.

He knew that intervention in Samos might mean war and was ready for war when it came. The representatives of Miletus who came to Athens to ask for Athenian help in their border dispute with Samos were accompanied by a number of Samian democrats who stated that the government of their island was planning to secede from the alliance and urged Pericles to replace the government with a democracy, a measure which would require the use of force. The Athenians, on the motion of Pericles, supported the claim of Miletus and sent forty ships to Samos. The move was too sudden to be resisted. The Athenians took a hundred hostages, mostly boys and young men of the leading families, and deposited them under guard on the island of Lemnos. In Samos they set up a democratic government and, leaving behind them an Athenian commissioner with a small garrison, sailed away.

However, they had miscalculated the strength and resolution of the anti-democratic party. Many of these had escaped to the mainland as soon as the Athenian fleet was sighted, had made their way inland to the Persian governor Pisuthnes, and had found that he was willing to help them. Since Persia and Athens were at peace, he could scarcely come out openly on their side, but the help he did give was effective: he put about seven hundred mercenary troops at their disposal. With this force they returned to Samos by night and, after overwhelming the Athenian garrison, killed or arrested most of their political opponents and then, acting with great speed, landed at Lemnos and took away the hostages. They handed over their Athenian prisoners to the Persians, having first branded them on the forehead with the Athenian emblem of the owl. This act of savagery led, as such acts usually do, to a retaliation that was equally savage, since in the subsequent fighting the Athenians branded their Samian prisoners with the mark of the *samaena*, a kind of warship which is supposed to have been designed by Polycrates and which used to be used in Samian coinage as the owl is in Athens. The fact that the Samians acted in such a way seems to indicate that they now considered themselves too strong to be attacked. They expected too that other members of the Athenian alliance would take the opportunity to revolt, so that if Athens did decide to act she would have to disperse her forces too widely to be effective anywhere. And in fact the important city of Byzantium, no doubt in collusion with the Samians, closed her harbor to Athenian ships and refused to make her contribution to the Athenian treasury.

The feeling in Athens was one of anger rather than

alarm, though there was indeed reason for alarm. Before this time people had enjoyed jokes to the effect that Pericles's only motive in championing the cause of Miletus had been his infatuation for Aspasia, who was of course a native of this city. They believed that since the crushing of the revolt in Euboea everything was secure, and, finding themselves disappointed, reacted with their usual violence. They were willing to give Pericles everything that he asked, and Pericles asked for nothing else than the employment of the whole force of the state. He saw more clearly than the rest the real danger of the situation and knew that with every day that passed without action the danger would increase. Neither Persia nor Sparta could be counted upon to keep the peace. Pisuthnes was already supporting the rebels and a deputation from them was on its way to Sparta. Particular anxiety was felt about the loyalty of Chios and Lesbos, since if their fleets were united with Samos and were supported by the Phoenician fleet under Persian control, Athens would be outnumbered on her own element, the sea.

All of the ten Athenian generals were required to serve on this campaign. Pericles himself set out at once with the sixty ships that were immediately available, once again taking a deliberate risk, since the Samians had a fleet of at least seventy ships and it would be necessary for Pericles to detach some of his own vessels to make sure that Chios and Lesbos would send their contingents and to keep a lookout for any possible move of the Phoenicians. The Athenians, however, believe themselves, with reason, to be the best sailors in the world and in all naval battles have shown themselves indifferent to odds. This was one of many occasions in Athens when men were called up and ships made ready for sea in a fever of hurry, impatience and enthusiasm. Many of those who served on this expedition were friends of mine. Sophocles was one of the generals. My old pupil Archelaus was in the infantry, as also was young Socrates.

There is no doubt that the Samians were surprised by the speed and daring of Pericles's action. They had imagined that Athens would either do nothing or would take some time to muster her forces and had decided to use what they thought would be an interval to settle their account with Miletus. But they were recalled from Miletus by fire signals announcing the approach of an Athenian fleet.

Pericles had already dispatched some ships to Chios and Lesbos, so that by the time he made contact with the enemy fleet of some seventy triremes his own strength was only forty-four. He engaged them without delay, defeated them and drove them into harbor. However, he still lacked sufficient naval and military strength to impose a regular blockade. A few Samian ships succeeded in slipping out of harbor and sailed southward to make contact with Pisuthnes and urge him to bring up the Phoenician fleet to their aid. This was a danger which Pericles took seriously. The Phoenician fleet would not move without the authority of the Great King, but Pisuthnes had already broken the peace with Athens and there were no means of knowing with certainty whether the Great King would approve or disapprove of his action.

Indeed, on this occasion the mere possibility of Persian aid did almost as much good to the Samians as the aid itself might have done had it been forthcoming. Pericles was soon reinforced by twenty-five ships from Chios and Lesbos and another sixty, with a strong army, from Athens. He was now able to land troops in sufficient numbers to be effective and proceeded to build fortifications to blockade the city of Samos itself. But before the fortifications were completed, reports came in to the effect that the Phoenician fleet had left Tyre and was sailing north. Pericles, with sixty ships, sailed to meet them. He had left sixty-five ships behind him, a force strong enough to contain the Samian fleet, and the fortifications seemed already capable of resisting any attack. His calculations were justified by everything except the event, though it is difficult to see how he could have acted otherwise. If a large Phoenician fleet were permitted to make contact with the Samians, Athenian difficulties would be enormously increased.

However, an opportunity for action, though a slight one, had been offered to the Samians, and they took advantage of it with skill and daring. They made their preparations quietly, manned their ships with remarkable speed, and suddenly attacked in full force the few Athenian ships which were watching the harbor, sinking some of them and putting the rest to flight. The rest of the Athenian fleet came into action hurriedly and was defeated, though with no considerable loss. An attack was also made on the Athenian camp and many prisoners were taken. The main fortifications held, but now the Athenians were on the defensive and for a fortnight the Samians had command of the sea. They used this period to bring in provisions and war supplies and to send to Sparta another deputation, which exaggerated their victory and urged the Spartans to act before it was too late.

The whole operation had been brilliantly conceived and carried out. It is interesting to observe that most of the credit for this goes to a philosopher. This was Melissos, who commanded the Samian forces throughout the siege and for whose military abilities Pericles professed a high regard. Indeed, as a general Melissos deserves great praise. As a philosopher he is interesting, but in my view unsound. He develops with great subtlety the doctrine of Parmenides that the whole is one. It is a doctrine which seeks to show, among other things, that all motion, all change, all becoming and passing away, all diversity is illusory, and it has always seemed to me remarkable that a general so noted for his rapidity of action should be one who believed motion to be impossible.

After a fortnight Pericles, with the main body of the fleet, returned. No trace of the Phoenician fleet had been discovered and he had heard nothing of the successful action of Melissos. Sophocles has told me that this was the only occasion in his experience when he had found Pericles impatient and almost resentful. He blamed himself for his long absence, though in fact it is hard to know how he could have avoided it; and he blamed the other generals for lack of forethought and energy. Characteristically, he never blamed the troops or the crews of the ships, since it was his belief that men under his command would always fight well if they were given adequate leadership. He even reprimanded Sophocles himself, who in an attempt to amuse him told him the story of how, at a banquet, he had been fascinated by the appearance of a beautiful boy who was pouring out the wine and, in a dexterous exchange of conversation, had induced the boy to put down his face to be kissed. "And after that," Sophocles had concluded, "you claim that I am no strategist." But Pericles was far from being amused. "In war," he had replied, "a general must keep not only his hands but his eyes clean."

The remark was unkind to Sophocles, who was in fact an efficient general, and most uncharacteristic of Pericles himself, who was always indulgent to his friends and seldom censorious of anyone else. That he made it at all is indicative of the most unusual state of tension in which his mind was at the time. For he saw, more clearly than others, the extreme danger of the situation and, being used to estimating the possibilities of the future, was aware that the whole

work of his lifetime was now in jeopardy. The Samians
were strong and confident. They lacked indeed the strength
to confront the full force of Athens, but if their success
could induce Sparta to invade by land and other states with
the strategic importance of Byzantium to revolt, Athens
would be unable to concentrate her power and, if she lost
anything, might lose all. I believe that Pericles considered
the situation at this time as the most serious of all in which
he had found himself, more dangerous than that which had
arisen after the Egyptian disaster or at the time of the revolt of Euboea. Even at the outbreak of this present great
war he remained perfectly confident, since he had every
reason to believe that so long as Athens would abide by his
policy she would be certainly victorious. He could see no
such certainty with regard to the situation in Samos, and
this I think was the only period of his life when he acted
with an impatience that was unlike himself.

There was, for instance, a most unusual decree passed by
the Assembly in Athens which, while not supported by Pericles (he was not in Athens at the time), was at any rate
not opposed by him. For two years the comic poets were
forbidden to criticize on the stage the leadership and conduct of the war. In many states such a provision in a time
of crisis would be normal and expected, but in Athens it
was absolutely unprecedented. For in Athens, while there
are the strictest regulations enforcing politeness in private
life, it has long been the tradition for the comic poets on
the public stage to enjoy complete license in the attacks
they make on individuals, however prominent they may be.
Indeed, many people are amazed to find that such license
can be tolerated by a people who in ordinary life resent a
deliberate insult more than anything in the world. Even an
offensive word may be punished in the courts, while to
strike a man, whether citizen or foreigner or slave, will

bring the most severe legal penalties. Yet no one thinks anything of abusing a general or a politician on the public stage. He may be accused of peculation, cowardice or immorality, and he himself is expected to join in the general laughter. Certainly Pericles had long been used to the jokes made about his infatuation for Aspasia, his parsimoniousness in private life, the peacocks bought for his mistresses, the strange shape of his head, his extravagance on musical entertainments and state processions, and much else. To my mind the inconsistency in this attitude of the Athenians is apparent rather than real. They are in all respects extremely sensitive to personal injustice, particularly as it may affect the weak and powerless. Consequently all men, and notably those unable to defend themselves, are protected by the law from all overbearing and insolent conduct by those who might be by nature aggressive, or, through an ignorant and insensitive opinion of their own wealth or power, regard themselves as superior to their fellow men. But the man who has already been recognized by the votes of his own people to be exceptional and deserving of power seems a fair target for criticism. Such criticism delights the hearers and can do no serious harm to one whose position is acknowledged in any case to be superior. Indeed, some of the more superstitious regard these public insults as being positively beneficial, since they may disarm what is supposed to be the envy felt for great men by the gods (a notion which, to my mind, shows a most unworthy feeling for divinity); while others, more rational, consider that it is useful to remind great men that they also are human.

Pericles was not only aware of this tradition, but approved of it. While he had the tenderest respect for the dignity of others and would often say that since even unkind looks can hurt, they, no less than insolent words and actions, should be punishable by law, he never resented criticism of himself and was curiously indifferent even to unmannerly behavior. There was, I remember, one occasion when some eccentric and boorish character, who had a fancied grievance against him, followed him the whole distance across Athens, shouting out abuse. Pericles paid no attention whatever to him until he reached the door of his own house at about the time it was growing dark. He then called to Aspasia and after he had kissed her, as was his custom, said: "I should be glad if you would tell one of the servants to bring a torch and light the way for my friend on his way home."

It is natural therefore that many people find it almost incredible that at a time when Pericles enjoyed such authority in Athens a decree should have been passed which limited to any extent the Athenians' prized possession of freedom of speech. I myself do not know how far Pericles was in favor of this measure, which, in any case, was only in force for two dramatic seasons; but I do not think that at the time he was actively opposed to it, and I regard this fact as conclusive evidence that he regarded the situation in Samos as the most critical and dangerous of all that he had ever had to meet.

They tell me that for the next few months he scarcely slept. When he was not actively engaged in the military and naval actions, he was sending message after message to Athens and to the loyal allies with a view to concentrating the greatest possible force in the smallest interval of time. He had no sooner arrived upon the scene than he led his fleet into action against Melissos and the Samian fleet. Here he took a calculated risk. Another defeat would have been disastrous, but so, in his opinion, would have been any hesitation in the pursuit of victory. His calculation was justified by the result. The Samians were routed and once

more penned up in their harbor. However, there still remained the dangers of Spartan intervention and of the
spreading of the revolt. Before either of these threats became a reality Pericles planned to bring the whole resources
of the state against Samos. In the summer newly elected
generals arrived with another fleet of sixty ships from Athens. Thirty more were supplied by Chios and Lesbos. Pericles now had at his disposal a fleet of two hundred ships
and an army of forty thousand men, together a greater
force than that which had been employed against Egypt or,
in Kimon's last campaign, against Persia. The generals too
were the most efficient, experienced and brilliant that could
have been chosen. Among them was Hagnon, an old friend
of Pericles's and one whom he regarded as the most careful
and reliable of all commanders. There was also young
Phormion, now at the beginning of his brilliant career. He
is known today, as the result of his recent victories, as one
of the greatest naval commanders that have ever served Athens, and Pericles was well aware of his ability and his
promise.

The operations on land were directed by Pericles himself, and now that he had secured a stranglehold on the
city, he acted with a care and a restraint which disappointed a number of his men who were impatient for revenge and would have gladly taken the chance of an all-out
offensive on the fortifications. But Pericles was still the
same. Now, as always, he was determined that not a single
Athenian should lose his life unless such a sacrifice was
necessary. Even as it was, many lives were lost, for the defenses organized by Melissos were both powerful and in-
genious, and the Samians, well supplied with food and still
hoping for outside aid, fought at first with confidence and
later with the recklessness of desperation. I am told that
Pericles himself showed the keenest interest in the devel-

opment of new techniques in siege warfare and apparatus. Here he employed the services of a fellow townsman of mine, Artemon of Clazomenai, who is, I suppose, the greatest mechanical engineer now living. He has told me that the knowledge shown by Pericles of the principles involved was unusual, but I was not surprised by this. Pericles had discussed with Pheidias the immense complication of weight, stress and tension which went into the building of the Parthenon, and I knew from the experience of our early life, when he and I together had spent hour after hour in scientific experiment, that he was one of those rarely gifted people who combine the keenest theoretical insight with patience and dexterity in practice. I should add that Artemon was equally impressed by the ingenuity of the defenses which were under the direction of the philosopher Melissos.

It was, of course, soon obvious that unless help came from abroad the position of Samos was, whatever the resolution of the defenders, hopeless. This help never came. No city in the Athenian alliance followed the example of Byzantium, and Byzantium itself was soon in difficulties. The Great King was satisfied with the peace of Kallias and had no wish to renew hostilities with Athens. He would prefer to have Greeks fight among themselves than combine once more against him. It was in Sparta that the Samians had chiefly placed their hopes and it was in Sparta that they were utterly disappointed. Had Sparta invaded during the first spring, the position of Athens would have been difficult indeed, and it was the fear of such an event that had led Pericles to bring into action at such speed so overwhelming a force. But the Spartans wasted this opportunity in debate. Their habitual caution encouraged them to wait a little longer on events; they could justify their caution by an appeal to legality, since to invade Attica would be to break the peace treaty; and after all, the Samians seemed to be doing quite well by themselves. In the summer, when the crops are gathered in, they are always reluctant to move; in the winter many of the roads are impassable; and by the following spring Samos had surrendered. The Spartans contented themselves with deploring the tyranny of Athens and congratulating themselves on that strict sense of duty in international relations which had prevented them from transgressing the terms of the peace. Samos was forced to capitulate, her fortifications were dismantled, her whole fleet taken over by Athens and her revenues pledged for many years in payment for the expenses of the war. The government was reorganized and hostages, of course, were taken, but there were no savage reprisals. Melissos, I am glad to say, still pursues the study of philosophy.

The news of the surrender of Samos caused in Athens, as was to be expected, a great outbreak of joy and exultation. People were heard to compare Pericles, in a favorable sense, with Agamemnon, the leader of the Greek expedition against Troy. It was said that while Agamemnon had taken ten years with the united force of Greece to conquer a not very considerable city in Asia, Pericles, with the Athenians alone, had in nine months reduced the greatest and proudest island of the Aegean. To compliments such as this Pericles was wholly indifferent. Indeed, he appeared to resent them. It seemed to me that some change, difficult to define, had come over him in the course of this year. He was, of course, beginning to grow old, but in no respect showed weariness or deficiency. He was at least as active as Kimon had been at his age. His views and his resolutions were unchanged, his mind as rapid and incisive as ever. Yet, though he would never shrink from any hardship or any responsibility, one could notice sometimes a kind of sad resignation in his eyes. He was at the peak of his glory, but glory had never meant much to him personally. Now it seemed to mean nothing at all. His mature satisfaction was in the greatness of Athens, but he had learned from long experience that no greatness can be permanently assured. He knew too that, in the nature of things, his life was drawing towards its close, and being aware of how frequently his own personal intervention had preserved and extended the power of this city to which he had given his heart, he may well have imagined with anxiety a future which he would be powerless to control. But if, as he grew older, his manner changed, it did not change, as often happens, in the direction of severity or hardness. Indeed, the strength and tenderness of his affections were perhaps more openly shown than ever before. I know this from my own experience and may be forgiven, perhaps, if I recall some personal events which, though they do me very little credit, will illustrate the kindness and understanding of my friend.

14

□□□□□

The End of Spring

I HAVE OFTEN OBSERVED that the most dangerous and difficult periods of our life, both physically and psychologically, are those times of transition between childhood and puberty, puberty and early manhood, youth and middle age, middle age and the beginning of old age. In these periods boys, girls, men and women are peculiarly susceptible to bodily ailments and to strange disturbances of the soul. We are accustomed to speak of the wildness and irresponsibility of youth, but here I think we exaggerate or distort, probably because of a wish to convince ourselves that we are now better than we were. This, in fact, is not generally true. Many young men and girls are at the age of twenty more able and intelligent than they will ever be subsequently, and it is very far from being the case that wildness and irresponsibility are confined to those of immature years. The worst crimes and excesses, the extremes of despair, the most manifest absurdities of conduct are apt to occur in middle or later life. We all know cases of apparently sober and law-abiding men of advanced age who suddenly and almost unpredictably become vicious or insane, who collapse into lethargy, luxury or dull despair, who become ridiculously infatuated with young girls or boys. Women are the same. Elderly and respectable matrons will show themselves totally incapable of exercising any restraint over their lusts — a subject, incidentally, which has been admirably dealt with by Euripides in his recent play *Hippolytus*. Indeed, in my view, our life tends to follow a pattern of comparative calm and growth set between short interludes of disruption, and the later interludes of transition are, contrary to general belief, the most dangerous. People will often accept this diagnosis in the case of women, whose physical structure and function most evidently alter with advancing years. But men are composed of the same basic material as women, and in men too we must suppose a constant rearrangement, a disappearance and replacement of the seeds or elements which, in their various combinations, shape and control the whole being. Here, as in everything else, it is intelligence alone which can bring and preserve order, and in human society this intelligence can be strengthened and reinforced by habit, law, example and convention. Yet in the best conditions the control is precarious and in times of disaster, terror and insecurity it is apt to be wholly ineffective. Very few men (and of these I believe Pericles was one) are able to live sanely throughout their lives.

Pericles was, I think, passing through the last of these difficult periods, which may be described as changes of life, at the time of the Samian war, and I have already given some examples of the unusual strain to which he was subjected. His character was, as I have said, quite unimpaired, as it had been during all those other transitional periods through which, since childhood, I have seen him pass.

The same, I fear, cannot be said for myself. I too, at this time, had become conscious of advancing age, and though

I had often observed the follies, miseries and mistakes of others in the same predicament, I lacked the necessary force of intelligence to bring order and resolution into the chaos and disintegration of my spirit. In a word, I fell into a condition of utter despair and resolved, weakly, to put an end to my own life. There were indeed extraneous factors which contributed to this insane resolution. None were important and it was the mere disorganization of my nature which compelled me, against my better judgment, to exaggerate them beyond all measure. I was deprived, for instance, of the society of my friends, all of whom were serving in the Samian war. I was in a state of abject poverty, having foolishly allowed myself to be defrauded of the little money which I possessed. Thus for some weeks I was almost entirely without food and as a result was constantly subject to fainting fits and long periods of total exhaustion. I could, indeed, easily have approached Aspasia or any member of Pericles's household, and my wants would have been immediately satisfied. Pride and despair prevented me from taking so obvious a step; for at the same time I had become profoundly dissatisfied with the whole endeavor and achievement of my life. It seemed to me that in all my long pursuit of truth from the time when, as a boy in Clazomenae, I had watched the shifting colors of the sky and sea, admiring nature and seeking for the causes of motion and of change, I had discovered nothing that was wholly verifiable, nothing, indeed, of any importance whatever. Most people from time to time are visited by such black moods and, with reason and courage, can surmount them. Both my reason and my courage were undermined by inanition, and I made up my mind to die. This was a most unworthy decision, for which I still feel shame. None of you, my friends, need feel apprehensive that I shall ever fall into such a state again, disgracing both myself and your hospitable city by suicide. I have regained the self-control which, in those days, for reasons both physical and intellectual, I had certainly lost.

I remember that I shut myself in my room, wrapped my cloak around me and, in a kind of torpor, waited for death. I was not impatient of its delay or apprehensive of its arrival. I scarcely thought at all and what thoughts I had may be described as pleasurable rather than painful. They arose from a cessation of all effort and an absolute resignation. I was aware of the noise of rejoicing in the streets which marked the return of the army from Samos, but I was unmoved by it and scarcely bothered even to wonder what had happened to my friends. It would be interesting to investigate further this state of mind, a state rather animal, I think, than human. However, that is not the purpose of this recollection.

I am dimly aware that at some time someone, perhaps a servant, perhaps an acquaintance, entered my room and spoke to me. Whether I replied to him or not I do not know, but if I did say anything, I should no doubt have asked him to leave and to allow me to die in the peace that I imagined I had acquired.

However, this solitary witness of my condition seems to have hurried to find Pericles and to have informed him that I was not only dying but appeared to want to die. Next I was aware of Pericles himself in my room, grasping my shoulders, pulling the cloak from my head and forcing me to turn my face to his. I seemed to see him from a great distance and to find him, with his gray hair and worn expression, scarcely recognizable. Behind the visible face I saw the face of the boy whom I had known in Salamis and I was bewildered by both the difference and the similarity. For some time I could not grasp the sense of his words. I observed with a faint feeling of surprise that his eyes were streaming with tears and that he was laboring under some emotion the cause of which I could not understand. Gradually I found myself listening with a dim understanding of what he was saying. He was grasping my hand between his two hands in a grip that was both firm and gentle, and his voice was almost breaking as he pronounced the words: "Anaxagoras, my dear old friend, have pity on yourself, have pity on me and on all of us. What is it you need? Who is it that has done you any harm?"

I shook my head and made no reply, but I had begun to feel moved by his manner, even though it still appeared to me so strange as to be incomprehensible. I listened half idly as he went on to speak of the great happiness we had found in each other's company, of the affection of my friends, of my scientific discoveries, of my duties to friendship and to myself. The voice seemed to come from a remote past, but as it continued, this past began somehow to grow nearer and to fill out into reality. Quite suddenly, and almost with a shock, I became aware of the precise situation — that I was lying in my room nearly dying and that Pericles, my friend, was being like himself in wishing to save my life. I found that I was smiling: "Pericles," I said (no doubt most feebly), "even a lamp will go out if it has no oil inside it."

Pericles sprang to his feet and now I could understand the mixed emotions reflected in his face. He was delighted that I had been induced to speak and he was horrified at the thought that, up to this moment, he had not realized that at least one of the causes of my collapse had been starvation. He made as if to leave the room and I, now strangely with each passing second renewing my vitality, felt a moment of dread at the prospect of being left alone. But Pericles did not leave me. He called for a servant, gave him some rapid instructions and came back again to sit on my bed. His happiness and relief were so evident that I too burst into tears. They were tears not only of shame but of joy. I wished to find words to thank him but, in my condition, he would not let me speak. Instead he loaded me with affectionate reproaches. Why had I not informed Aspasia of my state? Had I doubted his willingness to help me? Was I, against all reason, ashamed to gratify my friends by calling on them for aid?

As for me, my sanity and almost my health were restored even before I had tasted the food for which Pericles had sent. As soon as I was able to move he had me carried to his own house and kept me there for several weeks until I was fully recovered. He would visit me every day, and when he was absent Aspasia would be with me, or else some other friend; for Pericles had urged each one of our circle to show for me the affection which he felt. I will not attempt to describe my own deep emotions at this time both of gratitude and of shame. I have mentioned this incident simply to illustrate an aspect of Pericles's character which is known well enough to his friends, but is not apparent to those who think of him only as a general, a statesman and an administrator.

By the early winter I had fully recovered and even Pericles was satisfied that I should not relapse again into the miserable state from which he had saved me. That winter I attended the public funeral held for those who had lost their lives in the Samian war. These public funerals are a peculiar, and to my mind admirable, Athenian institution. The whole ceremony takes two days. The bones of the dead are collected and for one day remain in a tent. Here friends and relatives come and make whatever offerings they think fit to their own dead. Next day there is a great procession in which everyone can join, citizens, foreigners and the women mourning for sons, fathers and brothers whom they

have lost. The procession passes through Athens, skirting
the Agora and the public buildings, and goes through the
great new gate to the burial quarter outside the walls,
which is situated in one of the most beautiful suburbs of
the city. All Athenians who have fallen in war are buried
here with the exception of those who died fighting against
the Persians at Marathon. They were buried on the battle-
field, where the great mound which hides their bones is a
landmark which is likely to remain for ages. In the procession coffins of cypress wood are carried on wagons. There
is one coffin for each tribe and one empty coffin to commemorate those whose bones have not been recovered from
the sea or the battlefield. When the procession reaches the
burial ground, the coffins are solemnly laid in the earth,
while the women make their lamentations and utter their
prayers. Finally some famous man, chosen especially for
his powers of eloquence, mounts a platform and makes a
speech in praise of the dead to the assembled crowd, which
disperses quietly after the speech has been made. In this
way the Athenians pay the greatest honor they can to those
who have died for them. They also support from public
funds the children of the dead until they have come of age.

Pericles had on many former occasions been chosen to
deliver the funeral speech, and it was natural that on this
occasion too he should be the man selected. He was without doubt the ablest speaker I have ever heard, but in these
funeral orations of his he was perhaps more moving than at
any other time. This was due not so much to his skill as to
the depth of his sincerity. He valued life more than any
man and more than any man honored those who had given
their lives for Athens. There were splendor and sadness in
his words, and those who listened to him went away happy
in the sense that he had expressed and shared their sorrow,
while giving them true and valid reasons for pride in the

past and resolution for the future. It seemed to me as I listened to the speech he made after the Samian war that there was a more than usual sadness in his expression and in his choice of words. It was then that he used the phrase to which I have already alluded, "It seems to us that the spring has gone out of the year," and, momentarily, I imagined in him a kind of weariness as he looked back over so many years of unremitting struggle — the glories of the Persian war, the confident seaborne campaigns of his early youth, the victories and daring of Kimon, Myronides and Tolmides, the disaster in Egypt and the superhuman efforts to surmount it, Megara, Tanagra, Koroneia, Euboea, campaign after campaign, danger after danger, achievement after achievement. He seemed to me then like some brilliant charioteer, forced to drive forever his plunging and impulsive horses round a cruel track. Would the race never finish? Would not the horses stumble and his own knees grow weak?

I do not think that such ideas ever occurred to Pericles himself, though he was peculiarly sympathetic to the weaknesses of others and thus paid all the greater honor to those who were able to surmount their disabilities.

When he came down from the platform at the conclusion of his speech, he was greeted by one of the greatest demonstrations of affection that I have ever witnessed. Men crowded about him to press his hand or to touch his garments. The women covered him with garlands, as though he were some victorious athlete. The one dissident voice was that of old Elpinice, Kimon's sister. Her husband Kallias had died soon after the peace with Persia, and though she had grown children of her own, she seemed chiefly occupied with her memories of her brother. Certainly her loyalty to him did her credit, but it was marred by exaggeration, pigheadedness and a lack of justice. She had bitterly disapproved of the peace negotiated by Kallias. She blamed Pericles for Kimon's ostracism and gave him no credit for having passed the decree which recalled Kimon from exile and established him in his last command. Now she thrust her way through the crowd and, being a formidable and respected lady, succeeded in making herself heard. "A fine thing, Pericles," she shouted, "for you to be crowned with garlands! These brave men have lost their lives fighting against a Greek city and an ally — Kimon never led an army except against Persians, Phoenicians and barbarians."

The crowd began to show anger and impatience with the old woman, but Pericles smiled and spoke to her gently. He forbore from reminding her that her facts were, in any case, incorrect — Kimon had been the first to lead an Athenian army against an ally in revolt. He merely laid his hand upon her arm and said, "My dear Elpinice, you remember the verse of Archilochus, 'This gray head needs neither perfume nor garlands.'" He may have known that she was always peculiarly irritated by the playful attitude which he was accustomed to adopt towards her.

Now, as I look back at that time and at the times before it when we were young, I see more clearly than I did then the significance of the words "the spring has passed from the year," though I remember too that we were only conscious of a splendid summer. In the following year the Parthenon was completed, and at the great celebration of the Panathenaea the crowds were greater and more enthusiastic than any which had ever been seen in Athens. The festival, as you know, is the most splendid in Greece. It includes horse and foot racing, contests in music and poetry, and more than a hundred prizes are awarded to the winners of the various events. Not only the Athenians but members of the Athenian alliance take part in the festival and the sacrifices. Resident foreigners all wearing red cloaks also have their place in the great procession to the Acropolis with which the ceremonies conclude. In this procession the new embroidered cloak for the goddess, which has been woven and decorated throughout the year by Athenian girls of the highest birth and best reputations, is carried through the streets spread out like a sail on a model ship, a reminder, perhaps, to Athenians and to the world that the greatness of the city was won and is maintained on the sea. Representatives of the whole population escort the sacred robe. There are girls with baskets carrying the sacrificial implements, boys with pitchers, old men with olive branches in their hands, chariots, and finally a detachment of young men of the cavalry, the handsomest of their age riding the finest horses. This year there was more joy and excitement in the spectacle than ever before, for the robe was being carried to the new gold and ivory statue of Athene which was the great work of Pheidias. It is a figure forty feet in height and in the dark sanctuary it seems to burn and shimmer with a light of its own. The features are radiant and severe. It seems divine but also Athenian, and indeed in this whole temple the people of Athens seem to mingle with and become almost inseparable from the gods. On the sculptured freize are depicted the boys and girls, the young and old of Athens and they move with the grace, dignity and freedom of gods. I know of no other temple where mortals have such places of honor. Half the people, freemen and slaves, had taken part in the construction of this work. Their joy in their achievement was indescribable, and equally great was the admiration of guests and foreigners, all of whom were asking each other the same question, "What other city in the world could show anything so splendid?"

Greatness will inevitably produce envy, yet during the

days of celebration and dedication even envy did not show itself. All was joy, triumph and generous admiration. This was not a mood that could long continue. One soon began to hear again the old complaints that Pericles had squandered the resources of the allies on a display for which he himself was taking all the credit. Yet the niggardly and carping criticism was ineffective. The position of Pericles was more secure and unassailable than that of any statesman who has ever controlled the affairs of Athens. As had happened before, those who wished to attack him had to divert their attacks upon his friends. The victim they chose was Pheidias and the instrument they used was a cantankerous, vain and opinionated artist of the name of Menon, who had worked under the direction of Pheidias in the decoration of the temple and who, in his own opinion, was a great sculptor who had received insufficient recognition. Menon took up a position as a suppliant in the market place and, when people questioned him, said that he had information to lay against Pheidias, but was afraid to act against one who had such powerful friends unless his own safety and immunity were guaranteed. This was a clever move, since the curiosity of the Athenians is so great that they would rather condone a crime than be deprived of any scandalous information which the criminal is capable of producing. Menon was promised his safety and proceeded to accuse Pheidias of having diverted to his own use some of the gold which had been voted for the construction of the statue. Both Pheidias and Pericles treated this accusation with contempt. In fact the gold had been laid on in such a way that it could easily be detached from the statue. This was done and the weight of the gold was found to be precisely what it should have been.

This should have been enough to discredit Menon, but he still found an audience for his second charge. He now accused Pheidias of impiety and sacrilege. He pointed out that on the shield of the goddess, which was adorned with sculptures of the battle with the Amazons, could be seen likenesses of Pericles and of Pheidias himself. And indeed Pheidias had amused himself in this way. He had represented himself as a bald old man, struggling with both hands to lift up a rock, and he had also included a portrait of Pericles as a young man engaged in fighting with an Amazon. Here the likeness could be disputed, since the face of the figure was covered by an upraised arm, but the general character and bearing of the figure were certainly those of Pericles. To any intelligent man this performance of Pheidias must seem innocent enough, but, as I have every reason to know, the very mention of the word "impiety" is apt to affect a large section of the Athenians in a wholly irrational way. There was now no doubt that Pheidias would be summoned for trial before the courts. Pericles was perfectly willing to defend him, but even Pericles could not be certain that prejudice and envy would not be too great to be resisted. As for Pheidias himself, he had finished his work in Athens and was in any case anxious to take on a commission in Olympia, where he had been asked to make another great gold and ivory statue, this time of Zeus. He therefore refused the help of Pericles as an advocate and, wisely, I think, merely asked him for his assistance in escaping from Athens before the day of the trial was fixed. This was easily arranged and Pheidias reached Olympia safely. He died there during the early years of this present war, but before he died he completed the statue of Zeus, which many regard as the greatest work of his career.

The attacks of Menon had no effect whatever on Pericles himself. As soon as Pheidias had disappeared, the whole affair was forgotten. No effort was made to remove or alter the likenesses on the goddess's shield. They are there to be seen today. But both Pericles and I were saddened by this incident. First Damon and now Pheidias had been treated with injustice. Nor was Pericles pleased with his own immunity. It seemed to him particularly dishonorable in an enemy to attack his friends while shrinking from attacking him personally.

15

□□□□□

Before the War

I THINK THAT at this time no one (not even Pericles himself) imagined that peace would last only for the next
five years. Certainly it appeared to me that the long work
of Pericles's life was proving wholly successful and was established as securely as any human organization can be.
The administration of the empire was working smoothly;
taxation had been put on a more equitable basis; there
seemed to be no likelihood of any other revolt like that of
Samos. In Athens the great building program continued.
As soon as the Parthenon was finished, Mnesicles began
work on the great gateway of the Propylaea, a piece of architecture still not completed but even now of a splendor
and daring which can compare with the Parthenon itself.
The authority of Pericles was more secure than ever before.
Each year he was elected general and nearly always had his
friend Hagnon as one of his colleagues. Under their guidance the power and influence of Athens grew steadily
greater, nor was this growth attained by any infringement
of the clauses of the thirty years' peace with Sparta. As Pericles had foreseen, there was plenty of scope for Athenian

enterprise outside the Peloponnese. The effects of this enterprise would, in the long run, certainly alter the existing balance of power, but this alteration would come, he expected, peacefully and, as it were, naturally. The areas marked out for activity were the north, the northeast and the west. Different policies were pursued in each of these areas, and in all of them these policies appeared successful.

In the year when building operations began on the Propylaea, Pericles sailed out in command of a great fleet to the Black Sea. This was an expedition in which he took particular pride, since he accomplished much without incurring any but the most trifling losses. He appeared in these distant waters not only as an Athenian general leading an invincible fleet but as the champion of all Greeks against their barbarian enemies and their own oppressors. There are, as you know, great numbers of Greek cities on both the northern and southern shores of the Black Sea and many of them are under constant pressure from the tribes of the interior — Thracians, Scythians and others. Pericles showed that an Athenian fleet could sail anywhere unopposed and that the protection of Athens was available to all who needed it. A large proportion of Athenian imports — in particular corn, dried fish and iron — comes from these Black Sea ports, and in the course of his voyage Pericles was able to strengthen the ties, both political and economic, which united their interests with those of Athens. At the important city of Sinope, he intervened in a war being fought by the people of the town against their ruler, who had established himself as a dictator. Athenian intervention was enough to turn the scale and, in gratitude, the people of Sinope welcomed a colony of six hundred Athenians to whom they gave the full rights of citizenship. In the far east too, at Amisos, again at the invitation of the local population, another Athenian colony was planted and given the name of Piraeus. These, as Pericles was proud to say, were Pan-Hellenic actions. The power of Athens was being employed now, as it had been in the beginning, not to subjugate others but to increase and maintain their liberty.

Just the same policies were carried out in the following year by Hagnon, who took a large army to Thrace and, at the place known as Nine Ways, founded the great city of Amphipolis. Nearly thirty years had passed since the disaster in which ten thousand Athenian colonists had been massacred at this place, and as was natural, the success of Hagnon's expedition was greeted in Athens with patriotic fervor. The position is one of great importance and it appears that Hagnon has built and fortified the city in such a way that it is impregnable. It controls the main route from Macedonia to Thrace and is, I have been informed by young Thucydides, who has property in this area, most valuable as a center from which to exploit the great mineral resources of the district and the fine shipbuilding timber which comes down the river from the interior. Here too, as at Thouria, the policy with regard to the new city can be described as Pan-Hellenic rather than exclusively Athenian. Hagnon was the founder, but colonists were invited to come from all quarters and among these the Athenians form a minority.

All these operations were carried out in parts of the Greek world over which neither Sparta nor any of her allies could claim any right to exercise control. The same, strictly speaking, can be said of the operations in the west under the brilliant leadership of Phormion, although it is true that some of Sparta's allies, and in particular Corinth, were peculiarly sensitive to any Athenian action in the western sea. In responding to an appeal for help from the Acarnanians in the country north of the mouth of the Gulf of Corinth, Athens was infringing no existing treaty, nor, I think, did anyone suspect her, as some do now, of any design to occupy the islands in the Ionian sea and even the cities of Italy and Sicily. Pericles had indeed entered into alliance with some of these cities but these alliances were purely defensive. He had already clearly shown in the case of the settlement of Thouria that he had no ambitions for conquest in the west. And the foundation of Amphipolis provided further evidence that Athenian influence was to be extended peacefully and in a liberal spirit.

In no legalistic sense, then, can it possibly be maintained that during these years Pericles was deliberately planning war. Yet it would be foolish to deny that he was aware that at any time he might be threatened with war. He had too much experience and intelligence to be under any illusions in this respect. He knew the slowness of the Spartan mentality and that extraordinary arrogance of theirs which allows them to convince themselves that they must be, under all circumstances, irresistible. He knew too that among the Spartans there were some who were not wholly dull. These had only to open their eyes in order to see that as the power and prestige of Athens increased, so inevitably, whether or not the fact were to be admitted, must decrease the influence of Sparta in international affairs. He hoped that in the end this fact would be recognized and accepted. After all, the Spartans prided themselves on their restriction and had shown little inclination and no ability to transcend their self-imposed limitations. It was possible that so long as they were left undisturbed in the Peloponnese they would not notice, until it was too late, that the Peloponnese had become in fact and in the eyes of the whole Greek world something out of date and inconsiderable.

But this, though a possible solution, could not be depended on as a certainty. The only certainty was that

Sparta, if she wished to retain what she still considered her dominant position in Greece, would have, at some time or other, to go to war. It could be logically maintained that to do so would not be in her best interests, but men do not always act in their best interests. Fear and pride often overrule reason. Pericles, therefore, while determined to abide strictly by the terms of the peace, was prepared for war. He believed that, so far as any forethought and calculation can be relied upon, Athens would, if war came, certainly be victorious, and in any matter which in his view vitally concerned Athens, he would never make the smallest concession to Sparta. Yet he knew that the course of no war is predictable. Events occur which are beyond the reach of calculation and even the strongest can make mistakes which may prove eventually or immediately fatal. He was, I think, confident that, so long as he lived and controlled policy, such mistakes would not be made; but he knew that both his ascendancy and his experience were unique and he distrusted some of the rising politicians who, under cover of the name of democracy, were already beginning to vulgarize and to distort the precision and justice of his own ideas. Following Themistocles and Ephialtes, he had consistently promoted a policy designed to make Athens independent and powerful. His opponents had been those who had shrunk from enterprise either from fear of Sparta or of democracy or of both. Against these opponents Pericles had developed arguments to show that without empire Athens could never be independent and that to gain and maintain empire it was necessary for the whole people to enjoy and be trained in responsibility. But behind these arguments lay his considered views of nature and of human life. Empire was not an end in itself; it was the necessary means for bringing into reality the potentialities which he saw hidden in human and in Athenian nature. Power had to be exercised, but not for its own sake. Freedom, justice, generosity and the flowering of ability and genius were the ultimate aims. His aversion to and contempt for Sparta sprang from his conviction that what merits these Spartans had were imposed upon them rather by necessity and discipline than developed through freedom of choice and the true courage which can look in any direction. His views, I may say, were those of a philosopher who recognizes and admires variety and who, in imposing order, will allow for change, growth and motion.

In Athens, even by this time, there were few who grasped these views of his in their entirety, though many had been stimulated and ennobled by some glimpse or partial understanding of them. No one in my experience has understood them so well or admired them so fervently as that young Thucydides, the relation of Kimon, with whom I am from time to time in correspondence. But there were already others who, by appropriating for their own use some phrase or argument of Pericles, would wholly distort its meaning by taking it out of its context and, by robbing it of its complexity, reduce it to something simply untrue. There was, for example, Kleon, the rich owner of a tannery who claims to be a man of the people and who, I am told, now enjoys more influence than he did then, though even then he had a certain following. His authority was not, of course, at all comparable with that of Pericles, but what was both significant and dangerous about the little authority he did have was that he won it by representing himself as pursuing, with greater energy and realism, policies which in the past had been associated with Pericles himself. He was not only in favor of extending Athenian power and influence, but was for extending it extravagantly and by all means. He not only wished to keep control over the allies but openly demanded their subjection. He supported the violence of his opinions by making use of the commonest and most vulgar sophistries, in which he appeared actually to believe. He interpreted democracy not as being a state of affairs in which every man had the right and opportunity to develop in ability and virtue, but as one in which no one had the right to be more able and virtuous than anyone else. Yet at the same time he would declare it to be a law of nature that the powerful had always the right to impose their will, whatever it might be, upon the weak. Generosity was to him mere laxity, a wise consideration for others mere weakness and a waste of time. He prided himelf on being blunt and simple, an active realist rather than a hesitant intellectual, and was unconscious that his "realism" consisted in an inability to see more than a fraction of reality and that his "simplicity" sprang merely from his incapacity for discursive thought. One may imagine that such a character, while possibly able to win some support from that minority who habitually envy and resent the superiority of others, could never enjoy a considerable influence among so informed and versatile a people as the Athenians; and indeed people were more apt to laugh at him than to take him seriously. Yet with all his defects, he possesses certain qualities which could make him both dangerous and effective. He has boundless energy, all the self-confidence of the unreflective, and a kind of instinctive shrewdness which enables him to exploit any apparent weakness in an opponent and to exaggerate into a frenzy any passing mood or prejudice in his audience.

It was a new experience for Pericles to find himself opposed by one who claimed to be more of a democrat than he, and though he looked upon this vulgar travesty with the utmost contempt, he was fully aware that, though his personal position could never be disturbed by a man like Kleon, he would not always be present to counteract him and that a situation might arise in which, owing to either despair, disappointment or overconfidence, natural good sense could be overcome by violence and brutality if expressed with sufficient conviction and plausibility. He himself had known and had been able to restrain such moods, but he recognized their danger. "I am not afraid," he would often say, "of anything that an enemy could do against us. What I fear is only our own mistakes." It may well be, therefore, that with such characters as Kleon in mind, Pericles would have preferred to fight a war, supposing it to be inevitable, at a time when he himself together with those whom he trusted would be able to control it. But I do not believe that he did regard war as inevitable, even though he was more aware of its possibility than were most of us.

And indeed, when I look back on the events which are said to have provoked the war, I cannot see that any one of them or all of them together were of sufficient consequence to explain the event. The war is not being fought for the sake of Corcyra or Potidaea or Megara. It is much more than that. It is a struggle between two irreconcilable schemes of living. At long last the Spartans did recognize what Pericles had always known, that Athens and the Athenian way of life were certain to control and permeate the future unless Athens was destroyed. One may speak of Spartan jealousy and Spartan fear, and no doubt these emotions played their part. But the true cause is something more profound and is to be looked for in the nature of man himself and of the universe. It is something, I think, which was recognized by Heracleitus when he wrote: "Strife is justice," which I interpret as meaning that all life and all creation must, if they are to continue, perpetually advance into change, so that in a sense the future will always be at war with the present and the past. On the other hand, something of the past must be preserved and persist in some form even in change. Otherwise existence would be a series of discontinuous events, bearing no relation to each other and incapable of being either perceived or understood. There is, therefore, a necessary tension between two forces, a clinging to permanence and an impulse toward the unknown, rest and motion, peace and war. The nature of minerals is to resist motion and to deny growth; vegetables, while rooted in the same place, are capable of a variety of transformations; animals not only change and renew their structures but move freely from place to place in sea, air or on the earth. But of all things man seems to be most fitted for elaboration and invention. He alone can create and can choose, within limits, new and unexplored directions. Yet he too must have some of the qualities of a stone to ensure his continuity. Memory binds him to his past, tradition is a necessary basis for innovation. And he, being more conscious than a stone, a vegetable or a beast, being more sensitive to pleasure and to pain, feels with a particular severity the tension of the two forces on whose opposition his existence depends. He will find both delight and disquiet in innovation, and in lethargy he will find both peace and dissatisfaction. To create must imply disruption; to persist must be to repress. This truth has even found its way into our mythology, for example, in the story of Prometheus, which Aeschylus, in his old age, handled in a most philosophical manner. For Prometheus represents creation, liberty, transformation; he raises men from the mineral and vegetable state into the human and the divine; and as a result he comes into conflict with a god who controls what is and resists cruelly what is to come — Who is just? Prometheus or Zeus? Both Prometheus and Zeus are, as Aeschylus wisely recognizes, necessary, and in his play he contrives a reconciliation between them. But because both are necessary it does not follow that both are equally good.

The sympathy of an enlightened man will certainly be given to Prometheus, his liberator, rather than to Zeus, his oppressor; and even the mythological story insists upon the superior value, though not always the superior power, of innovation over a forced stability. For Zeus himself has not only won his supreme power by violence and by change but is certain to lose it unless he is able to adapt himself to a continued motion.

We find, then, in all nature and all human affairs a basis of necessary contradiction, but must not conclude that each opposite has an equal value. What is capable of motion and creation is to be judged as higher than what is not. Yet what is not will always be at enmity with what is.

If we bear these general truths in mind, we shall be, I think, better equipped to understand the causes of the present war and what is at stake in it. Athens and Sparta are both organizations of human beings and as such must depend on tradition and must grow by innovation. The existence of each is determined by this internal antagonism. But the two organizations are far from being similar. Each of them, it is true, has a strong sense of tradition or fund of inertia; but here all resemblance ends, because in Athens the creative and revolutionary element is so enormously more powerful and pervasive then it is in Sparta that, though in reality no organization of human beings can be static, one is almost inclined to compare Sparta with a stone and Athens with some winged creature. Here the disproportion is so great that it is impossible for one system to be merged with the other. Yet it would be better and nobler, were it possible, for a stone to become a bird than for a bird to become a stone.

Consequently I am, apart altogether from personal loyalties, on the side of Athens in the present war, and, though I would hesitate to forecast its result, I know that the Promethean qualities of Athens will, whether in victory or defeat, extend into and shape the future, while Spartan inertia can offer nothing but a kind of stability which, lacking a sufficient measure of the possibility of variation, cannot, in the nature of things, attain growth and must in time be buried or decay.

Of course the pretexts for the war, as distinct from its real causes, have a certain importance. It is possible to argue that if Athens had not allied herself with Corcyra, or if she had repealed the Megarian decree, the war would not have broken out, and it may be said that since the interests of Athens were furthered more by peace than by war, she made in these instances serious mistakes. This was not the view of Pericles. In his opinion the likeliest way of avoiding or postponing war was to make it clear that under no circumstances would Athens abandon any of her rights or make any concession to a threat. She would abide strictly by the terms of the peace and would be ready to accept arbitration on any point where the interpretation of these terms might be in dispute. In all other matters she would insist on her complete freedom of action. In making this guiding decision he was no doubt counting on the fact that the Spartans themselves profess to be, and in a sense are, great sticklers for legality and extremely cautious in making the first move in any conflict. But he knew that in the end Sparta would act, whether legally or illegally, in accordance with what she conceived to be her interests, and he thought, with much reason, that the best way to postpone this action was in the policy which he had followed throughout his life.

I doubt whether even he suspected that the naval battle in the northern seas between the fleets of Corinth and Corcyra, a battle which took place in the year after his triumphal expedition to the Black Sea, was likely to have any effect one way or the other on the future of Athens. Nor were the authorities in Sparta interested in this battle except insofar as they had done their best to prevent it. Certainly in Athens no strong feelings were aroused by the news that a fleet of seventy-five Corinthian ships had been completely defeated by a fleet of eighty ships from Corcyra. The Athenians had no great love for the Corinthians, who had been at war with them several times during this generation, but as the Corinthians had been invariably defeated, the Athenians, as is their way, bore them little resentment. Nor were they greatly interested in Corcyra. This island was indeed a considerable naval power capable of manning a hundred and twenty ships, but the Athenians had never feared such a power nor even wished to bring it into alliance with their own.

I would say therefore that the events which followed this battle were unexpected by almost everyone. It hardly seemed that even the battle itself had been fought for a sufficient reason. Its occasion was a quarrel between Corinth and Corcyra with regard to their respective rights in a joint colony of theirs, Epidamnus, on the coast of Illyria. Corinth, as the founder city of Corcyra itself, claimed an authority which Corcyra denied, having long been independent. Corinth, contrary to the advice of Sparta, had refused arbitration, had manned what was for her an exceptionally large fleet, had been disastrously defeated and had lost all control of Epidamnus. Here it was expected that the matter would end.

But this was, in fact, only the beginning. For the next two years the Corinthians applied all their energies to the building of a great fleet, to enlisting support from her allies and to hiring skilled steersmen and rowers from all parts of Greece. Large sums were offered in pay and many of these rowers came from cities of the Athenian alliance.

Athens made no effort to stop their enlisting. Nor did Sparta intervene in any way. She neither encouraged nor discouraged Corinth in her preparations for a war of revenge.

It was natural for the people of Corcyra to become alarmed. Corinth was building up a fleet larger and more efficient than her own; she was also receiving assistance from many states in the Peloponnese, though not from Sparta. But Corcyra had to depend entirely on her own resources. If she had only one enemy, she had no friends. So, before the two years of Corinthian preparation were completed, she sent an embassy to Athens, asking to be allowed to join the Athenian alliance. The Corinthians also sent an embassy to oppose this request.

On this subject there was a debate in the Athenian Assembly which lasted for two days. The arguments which carried most weight had nothing to do with the legality or illegality of an Athenian alliance with Corcyra, though much was said by both sides on this point. In fact, here the issue was perfectly clear. No mention had been made of Corcyra in the terms of the peace treaty and both Athens and the Peloponnesian states had a perfectly good right to conclude alliances with any state not expressly included in these terms. The real problem was a quite different one. It was a choice between two risks, the danger of antagonizing Corinth and through her Sparta, and the danger of allowing Corinth, by subduing Corcyra, to unite the Corcyraean fleet with her own and thus become a considerable naval power, capable of challenging Athens in the western seas. There were, of course, other considerations, but this was the only one that mattered.

Pericles, as is well known, recommended that a strictly defensive alliance should be made with Corcyra, and the

Assembly, as usual in all matters of importance, followed his advice. Since then I have often heard it said that by this action of his Pericles was deliberately precipitating war. Such a view is, I am convinced, mistaken and can easily be shown to be so. Had Pericles really wished to start a war he would have wished to start it with an initial advantage, and such an advantage could be gained with absolute certainty if the alliance made with Corcyra had been both offensive and defensive. A combination of the Athenian and Corcyraean fleets would unquestionably have destroyed Corinthian sea power for at least a generation. In fact Pericles, in his desire for peace and in his natural distaste for injustice (since an attack on Corinth would be a clear breach of the treaty), rejected this solution. On the other hand he was, as I have said, more conscious than anyone that war was a possibility, and he could not afford the risk of what might be in the end a combination of Corinth and Corcyra against Athens. It was impossible wholly to avoid both the dangers between which he had to choose. What he aimed at doing was to minimize them. By refraining from any aggressive action against Corinth, he would be keeping within the terms of the treaty; and by guaranteeing the independence of Corcyra, he would prevent the occupation of the island and the seizure of her fleet by a potential enemy.

In my view this policy was wise in itself and was immediately justified by results. In the first place only ten Athenian ships were sent to join the Corcyraean fleet and they were under the command of Kimon's son who had been given by his father the name of "Lacedaimonios" or "Spartan" and who was inclined to share his father's sympathies. Later it was felt that this token force might be too small to have any effect whatever, and twenty more ships were sent out.

All had instructions to avoid battle with the Corinthians unless an occasion arose when the Corinthians actually threatened to land troops on Corcyra.

In fact when, in the autumn, the expected sea battle took place, only the ten Athenian ships were present. So far as numbers were concerned it was the greatest battle that had ever been fought at sea between Greek states. The Corinthians had a fleet of one hundred and fifty ships and the Corcyraeans one hundred and ten. The action was fought near the coast of Corcyra and the Athenians who were present say that though the fighting was hard, it was of an extraordinarily old-fashioned character. Neither side seemed to have any knowledge of modern naval tactics or much skill in seamanship. In the battle the Athenians obeyed their orders. They came up to the support of Corcyraean ships that were in danger, but forbore from ramming any enemy ship until, late in the day, it became evident that the Corinthians were victorious and were preparing to land on the island. By this time seventy of the Corcyraean ships had been sunk, many of their men were taken prisoner and many on both sides had been killed. Only at this stage did the Athenians take a fully active part in the fighting, and by the evening they, with the remainder of the Corcyraean fleet, were preparing to resist a landing by the enemy. The victorious Corinthians had already sung their battle hymn and were moving forward into action when suddenly they began to backwater, to turn around and break off all contact. The reason for this surprising behavior was that they had sighted on the horizon the twenty Athenian ships which had been sent out to reinforce Lacedaimonios. Thus the mere distant presence of an Athenian squadron was enough to change confidence into fear.

The Athenians sailed into Corcyra unopposed and next day, with every ship that could be manned, sailed out to-

ward the Corinthian station. The Corinthians sent a messenger to lodge an official protest, demanding that the
Athenians withdraw and claiming that they were breaking
the treaty. The Athenians replied that the Corinthians
were free to sail anywhere they liked except against the territory of an Athenian ally. The Corinthians then sailed
home.

The results of this action were that both Corinth and
Corcyra had seriously weakened themselves, that the attempt to occupy Corcyra had failed, that Athens had
gained greatly in prestige without suffering a single casu-
alty, and that in no legal sense could she be said to have
broken the terms of the peace treaty. To my mind these
results are sufficient to justify the policy of Pericles, and it
was for different reasons that they were insufficient to prevent the war.

16

□ □ □ □ □

War Declared

INDEED, THE EVENTS in Corcyra had clarified rather than altered the existing situation. It is true that Athens had gained in strength, but she had been gaining in strength for years. Corcyra, therefore, is chiefly significant because it so emphasized this fact that Sparta and the Peloponnesians began to see it more clearly and to become more afraid of it.

It was natural that the Corinthians, after the ignominious failure of their great naval expedition, should attempt to do what they could in retaliation, but they were aware that they could do nothing considerable without the help of Sparta, and in Sparta there were for some time divided opinions. There was a strong party in favor of making war immediately, but many of the elder men, who could remember how in past campaigns Athens had suffered no irreparable damage and had indeed emerged from each of them as strong or stronger than before, were on the side of caution. The leader of this party was the old King Archidamos, a personal acquaintance of Pericles and one for whom he had some regard. Archidamos was prepared to admit that at some stage the interests of Sparta might demand war, but he understood the value of Athenian sea power and urged that before making any irrevocable decision, Sparta should equip herself with a navy strong enough to make some show of guarding her coasts and capable of intervening in aid of any Athenian ally which could be induced to revolt.

It seemed impossible to say which of these two parties in Sparta would prevail, but it was now generally recognized in Athens that there was indeed a danger of war, and the position of Pericles, who had long foreseen the possibility and long guarded against it, became, if possible, even stronger than before. Not that he was faced with no opposition at all. There were some (and these were the opponents whom he regarded as dangerous) who were for taking the initiative at once. Of these some talked of invading the Peloponnese before the Spartans could mobilize; others were for extending the empire into the west and bringing into the Athenian alliance the naval strength and manpower of the Italian and Sicilian cities. To such ventures Pericles was utterly opposed. His strategy had long been decided upon. In his view existing Athenian resources were sufficient to guarantee victory. She could be defeated only if she dissipated her strength in areas which were not vitally important or risked her manpower in a pitched battle against equal or superior numbers. He was aware, however, of the importance of the west and about this time renewed the alliances between Athens and some of the Sicilian cities. This in itself, he considered, would be enough to deter any of the other cities with pro-Spartan sympathies from sending ships or men to fight against Athens.

It was, as I have said, the rashness of those who were for doing too much too quickly which Pericles chiefly feared, and he was no doubt aware that in the Assembly he and he alone had the authority and influence to restrain them.

There were people like Kleon who in order to make themselves prominent would exaggerate every policy; and there were many young men, such as Alcibiades, who with little experience of war were eager for distinction and ready, in pursuit of it, to take any risk. When, as in the case of young Alcibiades, such people were not only inordinately ambitious but also extremely able and intelligent, they were likely to be, if uncontrolled, all the more dangerous because of their evident ability.

There were also, of course, a few, but not many, who out of hatred for the democracy or for Pericles himself would have welcomed at any price peace and the secure enjoyment of their possessions. It was, as a rule, members of this small minority who had in the past attempted to injure Pericles by prosecuting his friends. One other such attack was made upon him at this time. It was of a peculiarly cowardly nature and, though it did him no harm whatever, caused him great anxiety and great distress. Indeed, this attack seems to have been purely spiteful. No political purpose could be involved in accusing Aspasia of impiety and in raking up all the old stories, which no one believed, of Pericles's affairs with married women. The prosecutor in this case was the comic poet Hermippos. He had enjoyed a certain success on the stage and perhaps in this prosecution was as eager to advertise himself as to injure those whom he was attacking. The charge of impiety was based on an allegation that Aspasia had organized a party in which the girls present were dressed up as and called by the names of the nine Muses. In the course of the prosecution it was possible to make play with the usual stories about Aspasia's immortality and Pericles's amatory propensities. Hermippos employed his opportunity with his customary vulgarity. But more disgraceful still was the conduct of Pericles's son Xanthippus, who had recently quarreled with his father, as he was always doing, about money. This time he was offended because Pericles had refused to acquiesce in having his name used as a means of raising a loan for Xanthippus under false pretenses. Xanthippus now came forward and accused Pericles of having seduced his wife. By this action he hoped to revenge himself both on his father and on his wife, who not unnaturally disliked him intensely.

Aspasia being a woman and also an alien, did not, of course, appear in court. Pericles spoke in her defense, and I am told that this was the only occasion on which in public he allowed his emotion to get the better of him. Whether it was grief or anger that caused him to shed tears I do not know, but there is no doubt of their effect and that of his speech upon the jury. Aspasia was acquitted and from that time Hermippos ceased to attack her on the public stage. The reputation of Pericles was increased rather than diminished by the whole affair. As for his son, he never alluded to his evidence and never spoke to him again.

I mention this story not because it is important in itself but as an indication of how feeble at this time was any opposition that could be organized against Pericles. A few years later, when I myself was the object of attack, the situation had changed, but in the period immediately before the outbreak of war, his policies were accepted generally and his only fear was that there might be a demand for their exaggeration. There was little of what might be called a war fever, but there was no disposition to yield a single concession. Thus the great majority of Athenians had come, at least for the time being, to take exactly the view which Pericles had commended to them.

Though there had been little thought of war until the time of the debate on Corcyra, it now became evident to everyone that the likelihood of war was increasing every day. As was natural, people viewed the prospect with different feelings, but I observed no signs of fear or of anxiety. At this time there is no doubt that most of the young were looking forward to it. Alcibiades, for instance, now about eighteen or nineteen years of age, was displaying himself everywhere in new and particularly brilliant armor. He was as wild and extravagant in his ways as ever, but now, for the first time in his life, he saw the opportunity of distinguishing himself by courage and ability in battle rather than by his beauty, his drunkenness and his unexpected or outrageous behavior. His friend Socrates was delighted with the change in him. He was one of the few who had always maintained that Alcibiades was capable of exceptional virtue and nobility, and it is certainly true that in the presence of Socrates the young man did invariably behave well. One may say that Socrates is the only man whom Alcibiades genuinely respects; indeed he both loves him and fears him.

The attitude of Socrates himself toward the war was characteristic of the man. He was wholly indifferent to military glory, but it would never have occurred to him as possible that he should shrink from sacrificing his life if required by the city to do so. Both he and Alcibiades served in the campaign of Potidaea and indeed shared the same tent. In the first battle both distinguished themselves, and when Alcibiades, who had recklessly exposed himself in the fighting, lay wounded on the ground, Socrates stood over him, looking, they say, like a bear guarding her cub, and beat off all attacks until he could be carried to safety. Later, when the question arose of who should receive the prize of valor, Socrates proposed that the prize should be given to Alcibiades, and Alcibiades would have rejected it in favor of Socrates. The generals, bearing in mind the popularity of Alcibiades among the young and his noble connections in Athens, were glad to have the support of

Socrates in awarding him the prize, and Socrates was delighted that his friend's passion for honor and real merit should be so soon rewarded, being himself wholly indifferent to all honors. This story I heard later, from both Pericles and others. I have not seen either Socrates or Alcibiades since they set out on this campaign.

The fighting at Potidaea broke out, of course, before the open declaration of war. It did not in itself make war inevitable, but, like every event of the time, tended in that direction. Here again Athens was acting strictly within her rights, for Potidaea, though a colony of Corinth, is an ally of Athens in the tribute-paying class. The place is, as you know, of great strategic importance in the Thracian area and it was inevitable that Athens should be determined to keep control of it. So, when it became clear that the Corinthians in the town were intriguing with the King of Macedonia and with other cities and tribes in the neighborhood with a view to organizing a general revolt, it was only to be expected that the Athenians should demand that the Corinthian magistrates be expelled and part of the fortifications dismantled. The Corinthians, however, had raised a force of so-called "volunteers" and had introduced them into the city in good time. Thus the revolt of an Athenian ally was organized by Corinth, a city which was supposed to be at peace with Athens. Again there was fighting, this time of a much more serious nature than at Corcyra, between Athenians and Corinthians. In the battle the Corinthians were defeated, but they still held the town and Athens was committed to a long, difficult and expensive siege operation. It is only very recently that Potidaea has capitulated. Even before this battle, however, the Corinthians had appealed to Sparta for help, and it seems certain that some at least of the Spartan authorities had undertaken that Attica would be invaded unless the Athenians withdrew from Potidaea.

The Corinthians received support from other states. Megara sent a deputation to Sparta. So, in an unofficial way, did Aegina. The Megarians complained of the recent Athenian action in prohibiting them from selling their goods either in Athens or in any market of the Athenian alliance. The purpose of this "Megarian decree," which had been proposed by Pericles, was to show that it was dangerous for small states to take unprovoked action against Athens. The Megarians had supplied a contingent to the Corinthian fleet at Corcyra. They had given asylum to escaped slaves from Athens and they had joined the Corinthians in assisting the anti-Athenian party in Aegina. No doubt the Athenians also remembered the time when the Megarians had treacherously massacred so many of their men who had been garrisoned in towns held by Athens in Megarian territory.

All these complaints were used to the full by the party in Sparta which was determined upon war. Soon after the investment of Potidaea a congress was held to which all Sparta's allies were invited. Pericles realized at once that this congress would prove decisive for peace or war and he arranged to have in Sparta at the time some Athenian envoys, ostensibly on other business but instructed by him personally what to say if they could secure a hearing from the Spartan assembly. At this congress the speeches made by the Spartan allies were as might have been expected. The Corinthians, who without aid would certainly lose their army in Potidaea, made the bitterest and most energetic attacks on Athens. Most of the maritime states of the Peloponnese supported them and a few of those who lived inland and felt themselves in no way threatened advocated caution. Finally the Athenians asked leave to speak and were invited to do so. They had been instructed by Pericles to make the Athenian position so clear that there could be no possibility of misunderstanding it. In his view the danger of war would be increased rather than diminished if the Spartans were led to imagine that they could gain their objectives either by the threat of force or by any limited use of force. They were, he considered, most likely to be restrained by the thought that if they took any action at all against Athens, they would inevitably be involved in a war much greater than anything which they had experienced.

The Athenians spoke as instructed. Briefly they defended the acquisition and maintenance of the Athenian empire in words that Pericles might have used himself. It had been acquired by superior patriotism at a time when Sparta had declined her responsibilities; it was maintained for security; it was, in structure and policy, more liberal than any other empire that had ever existed, contrasting favorably in this respect with the domination exercised by Sparta over her Greek subjects. In no case could Athens acknowledge that a congress of Sparta and her allies had any right to control or even to criticize her policies. Athens was, like Sparta, an independent state. If there were disputes between them, these disputes should be settled by arbitration as was laid down in the terms of the existing treaty. Athens was perfectly prepared to submit to arbitration. If Sparta was not, then the responsibility for war would plainly be hers. If Sparta chose war, Athens would fight to the limit of her resources. It would be well for the Spartans to reflect on how great those resources were.

Obviously such words were not calculated to endear the Athenians to the Spartans, and some have suggested that the purpose of Pericles in instructing the ambassadors to speak in this way was to goad the Spartan assembly into a declaration of war. Such a view is wholly mistaken. It is characteristic of Pericles that he believed that even when dealing with Spartans the most powerful argument is truth.

He may have thought that in any case there was little chance of avoiding war, but he was convinced that the only chance there was lay in the clearest possible statement of Athenian resolution. It was impossible to appeal to the friendship of Sparta, but it was possible to count, to some extent, on her traditional caution and her reluctance to appear to be acting illegally. And in fact I am told that though the speech of the Athenians angered the Spartans intensely, it did have the desired effect of making them think.

After these speeches the representatives of the allies and of the Athenians withdrew and the Spartan assembly debated the question of peace or war. It is said that the old King Archidamos expressed admirably just those sentiments which Pericles had hoped might act as a restraining influence. While admitting the danger of Athenian expansion, he argued that it would be wise to reflect before committing Sparta to a war which might last longer than anyone expected and the result of which could not be foreseen. Though Sparta and her allies might prove superior on land, they were no match for Athens at sea and they were weak financially. Let them start at once to build a fleet and to collect contributions, as Athens had done, from their friends and allies. Then, in a few years' time, they would be in a position to fight a short and a decisive war. And in any case, he said, they should, before taking any irretrievable step, accept the Athenian offer of arbitration. Otherwise it would appear, whether rightly or wrongly, that it was Sparta, not Athens, which had broken the peace.

It is said that this speech had a considerable effect. But it must be noted that affairs had now reached the stage when the question was not a choice between peace or war but merely of when it would be profitable to begin the war. In such a state of feeling people are not apt to think or act with patience or deliberation. What they desire is a quick and simple solution to a problem which by making too great a demand upon their intellectual powers is filling them with anxiety. And the Spartans, more than all other people, delight in listening to some plain statement, however misleading, which will free them from the necessity of attempting to employ whatever critical and analytical faculties they may possess. Indeed, their pride in using only a few words derives from the great satisfaction they feel at not having to consider more than one or two ideas at the same time. Thus the speech of the ephor Sthenelaidas, in avoiding almost every important issue that had been raised, proved very much more effective than the well-reasoned appeal of King Archidamos. "The Athenians," he said, "are always making long speeches in praise of themselves. If they were good men at the time of the Persian wars, it is all the more disgraceful that they are bad now. All we want to hear is that they will leave our allies alone. On this point they say nothing. We must protect our allies. Therefore we must go to war."

He then, as presiding magistrate, put the question to the vote, and by a large majority the decision was for war.

After this there was an interval of nearly a year before hostilities broke out, since the Spartans and their allies needed time to make the necessary preparations. During this interval the Athenians put their defenses in a state of order, but made no hostile moves. The Spartans showed much anxiety at the prospect of being considered as the first to break the truce and, by diplomatic and other methods, attempted to create the impression that the war was a just one and that it was being forced upon them. These moves are of psychological rather than political interest. After the vote at Sparta, there was no further possibility of peace.

First the Spartans succeeded in securing a reply from

the Delphic oracle to the effect that "if they fought with all their might, the god would be on their side." Then they sent an embassy to Athens demanding that the Athenians should drive out "the curse of the goddess." This was an obscure reference to events which had taken place several generations ago, when a remote ancestor of Pericles had been put under a curse. No doubt the Spartans hoped by this demand to strengthen any opinion in Athens which might be opposed to Pericles. However, the support for Pericles was almost unanimous. The Athenians retorted with a demand that the Spartans should drive out "the curse of the Brazen House," also a somewhat obscure reference to a rather more recent act of sacrilege committed by a Spartan government.

Then a second embassy arrived to demand that Athens should give Aegina her independence, revoke the Megarian decree and abandon the siege of Potidaea. As was to be expected, Athens refused all these demands.

Finally Spartan envoys arrived who, without mentioning any of these subjects in particular, merely said, "Sparta wants peace. Peace is possible if you will give the Greeks their freedom." No one was impressed by this typical piece of Spartan hypocrisy. The army of the Spartans and their allies was already mobilized and, at the beginning of spring, began to move across the Megarian frontier into Attica.

17

The Last Years

I T IS NO PART of my intention, my friends, to describe the
events of the present war. I am doing only what you
asked me to do, which is to tell you what I can about the
friend whom I loved and whom I admire. From the time
when the Peloponnesians invaded Attica he lived for not
much more than three years, and for nearly two of those
years I had lost contact with him, being already at Lampsacus. Nor did anything happen in this period which revealed any aspect of the man which I have not already, to
the best of my ability, noted. Indeed, one of the things
most remarkable in him is his extraordinary consistency.
He behaved in this period of crisis as he had always behaved; he might have changed his views had there been
any reason to change them, but in fact every one of his estimates proved correct. The only event which upset his calculations was something wholly unpredictable, and he had
always stressed the importance of the unpredictable. His
only political disgrace (from which he soon recovered)
was caused by that precise failure of nerve among his fellow citizens of which he had already warned them in advance.

At the beginning of the war his authority was unquestioned. Some of his instructions were unpopular, but they were logical, definite, clearly explained and obeyed. He believed that Athens was invincible so long as her manpower was not dissipated and her navy retained control of the seas. Nothing predictable, except recklessness or impatience, could, he believed, do her any vital damage. He marked out and explained his strategy from the beginning. Like all his thought, it showed the precision and daring of one who sees clearly and distinctly what is essential and what is not. He told the Athenians that their possessions were everywhere in the world which could be reached by their ships. Their farms, their country houses, their land in Attica was expendable. What was not expendable was their manpower, their navy and their empire. Thus they were to avoid any pitched battle with the whole Peloponnesian army and, so far as operations in Attica were concerned, were to content themselves with using their cavalry to cut off isolated enemy detachments and to interrupt his supplies. Each year fleets were to sail to the Peloponnese to ravage the coasts and set up fortified bases from which further operations could be launched. He warned the people that the months during which they would have to abandon their farms and take refuge behind the fortifications of the city would be arduous and that they must be prepared to face some losses. But they must recognize that the loss of houses and of crops was quite inconsiderable. These could be rebuilt and resown, and meanwhile all the land in the world that was in reach of the sea was at their disposal. If anyone suffered from lack of food it would be the Peloponnesians, who imported nothing and who, by invading Attica, would be neglecting the cultivation of their own fields.

So, as soon as it was known that the enemy army was approaching, the Athenians in the country districts drove

off their livestock to the coast and ferried them over to
Euboea and other islands. They themselves, taking with
them whatever household belongings they could carry,
came into the city. The more fortunate were able to find
lodgings with friends or relations, but the majority had to
camp in the various parks or temples and on the ground
that was not built over in Piraeus and near the long walls.

This procedure has been followed every year when there
has been an invasion and by now the Athenians accept
the situation as almost natural. After the enemy armies
have withdrawn they return to their property, rebuild what
they can, drive back their flocks and cattle and resume, so
far as possible, their normal life from the autumn until the
following spring. But in this first year of the war everything
seemed strange and almost unbearable. The Athenians who
live outside the city walls are very attached to their property, their local shrines and the whole tradition of each
neighborhood. They are indeed proud of Athens but still
have, as is natural, a deep affection for their own villages,
each one of which likes to regard itself as being in some
way superior to all the rest. Moreover, they are used to security and to success. Now only the older people could remember the time of the Persian invasion, when not only the
country but the city itself had to be abandoned. They had
never seen, as Pericles and I had seen, smoke rising into the
sky of Attica from the destruction of their own homes. So,
though they might be logically convinced of the wisdom of
Pericles's policy, the results of carrying it out seemed to
them almost intolerable. There was indeed all the discontent which Pericles had predicted. "What sort of a general
is this," people were constantly saying, "who has an army
and does not use it?"

In fact, Pericles used the army exactly as he had intended to do. While the Peloponnesians were still in Attica,

he sent out a fleet of a hundred ships with a thousand hoplites and a large force of bowmen to raid the enemy coast.
This force did at least as much damage as the enemy had
done in Attica and perhaps caused an equal amount of anxiety, since no one could tell where it would strike next.
Meanwhile three thousand hoplites were still engaged in
the siege of Potidaea; many more were occupying posts in
Attica and manning the fortifications of Athens herself.
And later in the year the Athenians could at least feel the
satisfaction of having retaliated in full for what they had
suffered themselves. During the summer they expelled the
whole population of Aegina and resettled the island with
Athenian colonists, and, after the Peloponnesians had withdrawn, Pericles himself with a large army invaded the territory of Megara and laid waste the whole country, thus
demonstrating that the Spartans were unable to defend
their allies.

So, by the end of the year, much of the discontent which
had been felt against Pericles during the first few months
had disappeared. Indeed, to any intelligent man the value
of his strategy was evident. Athens had lost some property
but few men; she had done more damage to the enemy
than she had suffered; she had shown that, while her enemies could operate for only a short time and in one place,
her own forces could strike wherever they chose and at any
time. When, at the end of the year, the question arose of
who should be chosen to deliver the customary speech at the
state funeral of those who had lost their lives in the war,
the people unhesitatingly chose Pericles again for this
honor. The speech he made on this occasion was the most
moving and, I may say, the grandest that I have ever heard.
He did not say a word to justify his own detailed policy.
His aim was to do honor to the dead and to convince the
living that, though life was indeed precious, they had died

for something more precious still. Athens, to his mind, was not only great, but was absolutely unique. I believe his view to be a correct one. Certainly when Pericles (or, for that matter, Sophocles or Euripides) speaks of Athens, the words used are wholly different from what is usual in patriotic literature or declamation. Victory, courage, resolution, honor are the usual themes, but these Athenians will also and most markedly lay claim to other qualities such as wisdom, beauty, versatility and perfection. In this first year of war a new play by Euripides, *Medea,* was performed. It received only the third prize, largely, I think, because the audience was offended by the psychological complexity of the main character. But to one of the choruses everyone in the theater listened with a most profound pleasure and a strange reverence. In this chorus Euripides seems to have expressed both the antiquity of Athens and her dazzling modernity. It runs, to the best of my memory, as follows:

From of old the children of Erechtheus are
Splendid, the sons of blessed gods. They dwell
In Athens' holy and unconquered land,
Where sacred Wisdom feeds them, and they go gaily
Always through that most brilliant air where once, they say
That golden Harmony gave birth to the nine
Pure muses of Pieria,

And beside the sweet flow of Cephisos' stream,
Where Cypris sailed, they say, to draw the water,
And mild soft breezes breathed along her path
And on her hair were flung the sweet-smelling garlands
Of flowers of roses by the Loves, the companions
Of Wisdom, her escort, the helpers of men
In every kind of excellence.

This, my friends, was the Athens which I knew and was so soon to lose. Not that my own calamities, which have ended in a happy and peaceful life at Lampsacus, are of the slightest significance. What moves me most when I think of the great and proud words of Pericles and of Euripides is that they were true when they were spoken and may still be true, even after the misery and disappointment which fell on the city, and on Pericles himself.

For the next year started in confidence and ended in hysteria, lawlessness, terror and persecution. The Athenians have never been afraid of their enemies; if they suffer a defeat, they redouble their efforts for victory. Now, however, they were faced with a danger against which they could not fight and an enemy whose attacks were sudden, incalculable and irresistible. Those who had died in battle during the first year of the war were not numerous and they were buried in state. Those who in the second and third years died of the plague were almost innumerable; their bodies lay about the streets, where not even birds of prey or scavenging dogs would touch them, choked the cisterns or, if buried at all, were buried hurriedly and indecently.

Soon after the Spartans invaded Attica in the spring, the first deaths from this disease, hitherto unknown, were reported from Piraeus. Within a week it had spread to the upper city, where people began to die like flies. The death, moreover, was peculiarly painful and, in all its different forms, horrible to witness. Some died raving with thirst or fever, others from perpetual vomiting, ulceration of the bowels and sheer weakness. Very few of those who caught the disease recovered from it and there was no knowing who would catch it and who would avoid it. The rules of health commended by doctors appeared wholly ineffective; indeed, more doctors died in the course of their work than any other class. Equally ineffective were prayers and offerings to the gods. Nothing could be depended upon for protection; the healthy were as prone to infection as the unhealthy; those noted for their piety died together with

criminals and blasphemers. It was a situation in which all
the decencies, the mutual confidence and the conventions
on which civilized life depends were powerless to guide, to
stimulate or to restrain. Something was occurring which
was beyond custom and beyond understanding, and without custom and understanding, human nature must lose integrity and fall into chaos. In individual cases terror, fear
and bewilderment led to despair, abject cowardice, reckless desperation, apathy or vice according as character, circumstances or physical constitution differed. There were
few indeed who throughout this period were able to retain
their virtue, their courage and their good sense; and, as
might be expected, this general deterioration continued to
spread as time went on. This was not a calamity to which
one could become used.

At the beginning the Athenians continued to prosecute
the war with vigor. While the Spartans were still in Attica,
Pericles himself, with a hundred and fifty ships carrying a
large force of infantry and cavalry, sailed for the Peloponnese. Just as the fleet was about to sail and Pericles was
boarding his flagship, there was an eclipse of the sun. Had
this event taken place later in the year or, indeed, had this
expedition been commanded by anyone else, it seems likely
that the whole effort would have been paralyzed by superstitious terror. Even as it was, the helmsman of Pericles's ship
was too frightened to give the necessary orders. Pericles
then took off his general's cloak, held it in front of the
man's eyes and said, "Do you regard this as a terrible
omen?" The helmsman owned that he did not and Pericles
next asked him, "Is there any difference between this and
the eclipse, except that the eclipse has been caused by something bigger than my cloak?" Then he himself gave the
order for the libations to be poured and, as the sun's light
was renewed, the fleet set out with confidence. As in the

previous year they did more harm to the enemy than the enemy could do to them in Attica. But neither they nor the Spartans could do such harm as was being done by the plague.

When Pericles returned from this expedition, he found that the Spartans had retreated, no doubt fearing that they themselves might become infected, and that the plague had taken a firmer hold upon the city. He therefore decided to stay in Athens himself. The army and fleet which had been ravaging the Peloponnese were put under the command of Hagnon and sent northward to reinforce the army before Potidaea. However, some of these troops had already caught the disease and they carried it with them to Potidaea and to the men there. Within six weeks Hagnon had lost a quarter of his men, and he could do nothing but return to Athens, having achieved nothing valuable.

And now, with the sight and smell of death everywhere about them and with each man fearing for his own life, with homes and farms destroyed and not even the encouragement of victory in war, the Athenians, unable to understand how such sufferings had so suddenly come upon them, sank into a mood of utter despondency, enlivened only by bitterness and irritation. If they thought of the war at all, they thought only in terms of making peace at almost any price. Wishing to make someone other than themselves responsible for their irresolution and for their undeserved miseries, they began to blame Pericles for everything that had happened. He might, they said, have prevented the war altogether — forgetting that they themselves had voted for it. Or he might have adopted a different strategy. It would be better to die in battle against the Spartans than to perish cooped up behind fortifications in quarters that had only ceased to be overcrowded because of the number of deaths. Or perhaps, it was said, there might be some truth in the view that the house of Pericles was under a curse.

The attacks on Pericles began, as in the past, with attacks upon his friends. I was one of the first victims, being accused of impiety and of pro-Persian sympathies. There is no need for me, whom you all know, to comment on the absurdity of these charges which, of course, were only made in an effort to discredit my friend. Pericles himself, worn out as he was with continual work and anxiety, would willingly have defended me in the courts, but he knew that his own position was now weaker than it ever had been and was afraid that now his public intervention might do me more harm than good. I remember the gentle smile with which he said, "You used to teach me always to put first things first. In this situation what comes first is your life." So, as you know, I took his advice. He still had power enough to give orders that would be obeyed. He put at my disposal a ship which brought me to Lampsacus and there entrusted me to the kindness of those of you who are his friends. This is not the time for me to attempt to thank you for having acted toward me with all the generosity which Pericles himself could have desired. Nor is it important to dwell upon my personal feelings as I said good-by to him. If I say that I felt more concern for him than for myself, I may appear to be indulging in some boastful affectation; but if you knew him and loved him as well as I did, you would believe that I was speaking no more than the truth.

I never saw him again. The little that remains for me to report is therefore based on hearsay, but my sources are reliable. I have had regular news from Hagnon and have also received some most moving and clear accounts of events from young Thucydides, who caught the plague himself but fortunately recovered. He is not alone in the devotion he feels for Pericles, but he is remarkable for the clarity of his understanding.

It seems that very soon after I escaped from Athens, Pericles called a meeting of the Assembly. He spoke with his usual authority to an audience which, though almost entirely hostile, still listened to him with respect and followed his arguments even though they were determined not to be sympathetic to them. He spoke with deep feeling of the sufferings to which everyone was exposed and he spoke with humor of the angry criticism which was being leveled against himself. If, he said, he was going to be blamed for every piece of bad fortune that came their way, then he should expect to be praised for every stroke of good luck too. They might as well praise or blame him according to the state of the weather. As for his power, they knew perfectly well that he would willingly relinquish it if they could find someone else more capable of using it wisely in the interests of them all. But his chief aim in this speech was to give back to them their courage and resolution and to make certain that there would be no more talk of making a dishonorable peace. He told them that even now they had no conception of their own power. The whole world, he said, could be divided into two parts — the land and the sea — and over the whole of one of these parts they were supreme. The possession of this power was in a wholly different category from the ownership of land or houses. So long as they remained free they could easily recover everything that they had lost, but if they once allowed themselves to submit to the will of others, they would lose everything which they still had. There should be no question of sending embassies to Sparta. What had made the Athenians great was their capacity to bear misfortune with the utmost courage and to react against it with the utmost vigor.

The Athenians on this occasion acted in a manner which was strangely illogical but, considering their varied emotions and unprecedented sufferings, not more perverse than any student of human nature might expect. They were so used to relying on the judgment of Pericles and to following the precision and certainty of his arguments that they once again accepted the truth of his analysis and from that time had no more thoughts of peace but showed a renewed energy for the war. On the other hand they found it essential that someone other than themselves should be held responsible for the sufferings which they could not understand and which yet persisted, since it was still the height of the summer and it was not till the early autumn that there was any diminution in the violence of the plague. So they deposed Pericles from his position as general and sentenced him to pay a large fine in money.

For the first time in fifteen years Pericles was no longer in charge of affairs, though in fact those who were in charge were consistently following his policy and would continually seek his advice. Pericles, so Hagnon told me, bore his disgrace with dignity. He had gained the only point that seemed to him vital — namely, that the war should continue to be fought with resolution; and before the end of the year Potidaea had capitulated and Phormio had won a brilliant naval victory in the Gulf of Corinth, demonstrating once again the complete ascendancy of Athenian seamanship.

But in his private life Pericles suffered as much misfortune as anyone else. First his sister died of the plague and then his two sons, Xanthippus (with whom he had never become reconciled) and Paralos. His family was now extinct, since his son by Aspasia, young Pericles, was disqualified from citizenship. They say that when, at the funeral of

Paralos, his father laid a wreath on the dead body, he was unable to restrain his tears. Only once before had he been known to show his grief in public.

Soon afterward Pericles himself caught the plague and for some weeks his friends despaired of his life. During this time there occurred a complete reversal of feeling among the Athenians. They had been heartened by their victories and by the fact that in the cooler weather fewer and fewer people were becoming infected with the plague. Now they began to regret what they recognized as their ingratitude to the man who had led them for so long and, even in disgrace, had continued to inspire them. They were sorry for his private misfortunes and considered that they themselves would be dishonored if he were to die with his power and reputation diminished. Just as they had blamed Pericles for decisions which they had made themselves under his guidance, now they began to blame those others who had persuaded them to disgrace him. Every day people inquired earnestly as to his condition, and when it was known that he had a good chance of recovery they rejoiced almost as though one of their own sons or brothers had been restored to life.

I hear that the members of Pericles's own circle remained without exception loyal to him throughout this time. Even young Alcibiades, who had returned with a brilliant reputation from Potidaea, behaved with a gentleness and consideration which surprised all who in the past had often been shocked at the young man's levity and impatience in his relations with his guardian. It was Alcibiades, they say, who was most urgent in supporting Hagnon and others in their appeals to Pericles to stand again for the generalship in the following year, and I believe that he did this not so much from his personal ambition for the splendor of his own family as because he genuinely believed that

Athens could not do without the services of one whom, in the past, he had been accustomed to describe as "the old man." And I am sure that it was from a sense of duty rather than for any further desire for power or glory that Pericles did consent to offer himself for re-election.

The people were anxious and proud to restore him to all his old honor, and in sympathy for his losses, they passed a decree by which his illegitimate son Pericles should be granted Athenian citizenship. It seems that this act gave Pericles more pleasure than anything else.

He was still too weak to engage in active service but continued to attend all meetings of the war council until it became clear that his recovery had been only partial and that his health had been permanently undermined. He lay sick at home and scarcely capable of movement for some weeks before he died. Though toward the end he was almost too weak to speak, he retained the full use of his mental powers and the grace and gentleness of his manner were the same as ever. They say that shortly before he died Aspasia, who in her distress tended to be, like most women, superstitious, hung around his neck when he was sleeping some kind of charm or amulet. When Pericles opened his eyes, he smiled at her and said, "I really must be ill, if you think I shall take this sort of nonsense seriously."

When he was at the point of death, many of his friends were at his side. They tried to please him by speaking of his triumphs and victories, the trophies he had set up, the expeditions he had commanded. He surprised them by speaking, though he could only faintly utter the words. "I am not proud of these things," he whispered — "most of them depend on chance. I am proud because no Athenian has ever had to put on mourning because of me."

So my friend died. Next year at the dramatic festival Euripides won the first prize with his play *Hippolytus*. As the chorus spoke the last words, the audience rose and stood in silence, since they regarded these words as a reference to the dead man and to their own sorrow:

> This is a grief that is common to all of us,
> And came unexpected.
> Many the tears that now will be falling,
> Since for great men mourning voices
> Still last longer.